The Common S
of Teaching Mathematics

Caleb Gattegno

Educational Solutions Worldwide Inc.

First published in the United States of America in 1974. Reprinted in 2010.

Author: Caleb Gattegno

ISBN 978-0-87825-220-6

Educational Solutions Worldwide Inc.
2nd Floor 99 University Place, New York, N.Y. 10003-4555
www.EducationalSolutions.com

Acknowledgments

I wish to express my deep gratitude to my colleagues for improving the language which in the original text was often obscure. First I must thank David Wheeler whose acquaintance with my work goes back over twenty years and who has been responsible for editing the whole book; second, Ms. Caroline Chinlund for working on the original of some of the chapters, and Ms. Zulie Catir for re-reading the typed texts as often as was needed. My secretary Ms. Yolanda Maranga typed the text a number of times over the last four years. She deserves my thanks for her skill and patience.

Table of Contents

Foreword 1

Part I: Actions Which Generate Numerals 5

1 The Set of One's Fingers 7
2 Reading and Writing Numerals in any Base 25
3 Exploiting Complementary Numerals 39
4 Introducing One Aspect of Division 53

Part II: Actions Which Generate Algebra 59

5 A Model for the Algebra of Arithmetic 61

Part III: Numbers as Numerals Provided with an Algebra 77

6 Integers and Fractions 79
The Generation of Integers and Fractions 79
7 The Mathematics of Numbers 91
1 Prime Factors 94
2 Common Factors and Common Multiples 96
3 Towers and Sets 100
4 Powers and Roots 101
1 Polynomials 103
2 Exponents 111
Fractional Exponents 113

Negative Exponents 114
3 Logarithms 115

Part IV: Teaching Mathematics 121

8 Teaching Mathematics to Teachers 123
9 Teaching Mathematics to Children 141
10 Generating a Mathematics Curriculum 155
The Characteristics of Gattegno Mathematics, Books 1—7. 156
Fractions 158
Fractions as Operators 158
Ordered Pairs 160
Classes of Equivalence and Operations 161
Addition 162
Multiplication and Equivalence-M 165
Decimals 169
Percentages 172
Summing Up 172

Postscript 175

Appendix A: A Prelude to The Science of Education 177

Appendix B: A Map of Elementary Mathematics Derived From Tables of Partitions 191

Books and Materials 199

Foreword

For some time I have had it in mind to write a book which would substantiate my claim that it is now possible to make the study of education properly scientific. It seems to me at this moment that my contribution to the study can best be put in the form of several short books, each devoted to a particular part of the educational field, rather than, as I originally thought, into a single comprehensive volume. I offer this book as the first in such a series; in it I restrict myself to elementary mathematics, and mainly to the algebra and theory of numbers.

Perhaps this book will seem to others to be mainly another book about mathematics teaching continuing a line of development I have already exemplified in other writings; for me, it represents a radical departure. Now I know that *only* awareness is educable, I have found it possible to come up with original answers appropriate to many of the areas of educational endeavor — answers of a universality which ensure that they are, indeed, solutions to problems and not merely bright ideas. What characterizes this book is that it is concerned with people becoming aware of how to use their own manifestations, as perceivers, actors, verbalizers and thinkers, in order to gather mathematics on the way. It must therefore serve any learner of mathematics, whoever he is.

The study of the education of awareness has yielded tools which can be used to grasp unequivocally the whole universe of education: the method of investigation coincides with the field of application, and knowing replaces knowledge as the cardinal notion. Since knowing produces knowledge, but not the other way round, this book shows how everyone can be a producer rather than a consumer of mathematical knowledge. Mathematics can be owned as a means of mathematizing the universe, just as the power of verbalizing molds itself to all the manifold demands of experience.

In this book I show mathematization in action, giving only just enough detail to display what it is, and leaving the elaboration of these sketches to the reader. In this way he will find how much he has learned through the extent to which he can add to its content himself.

It is obvious that learning anything always exacts a price — the learner must always give some of his attention, his effort and his time in exchange for learning. It is also obvious that where spontaneous self-generated learning is concerned the learner willingly pays what is required, whereas in school he often does not. My contention is that he cheerfully pays up when the learning he wants to acquire dictates the price, but that he will refuse if the price is higher than it need be, or if he is offered the wrong goods in exchange. One criterion, I suggest, for the validity of the existence of a science of education is in its ability to make accurate estimates of the cost of learning.

Making the cost fit the learning requires that we know, in detail, what elements must be offered to the learner of a topic because he does not already have them and cannot invent them, and must therefore pay for. In an article, "A Prelude to the Science of Education," reprinted as an Appendix to this volume, I discuss this matter fully and show how "units of learning" can be precisely calculated. A consequence of the analysis is that we also know exactly what does *not* have to be offered by anyone because the learner is able to invent it for himself.

A second aspect of the cost of learning is what is required of an individual learner for him to become the master of what he learns. Here it is not possible to predict exactly what each learner will need to pay, since much will depend on him, but where the matter involved is a skill, as in most of the mathematics discussed in this book, we need to know that mastery demands practice, and that awareness must precede practice. Teachers can minimize this feature of the cost of learning by finding those situations which carry the correct awarenesses and by suggesting exercises which provide the facility that shows that the awarenesses are functional. The book gives many examples to show how this can be done.

In restricting the scope of this first volume to elementary mathematics it is my hope that many teachers of elementary school can be helped to abandon their belief that mathematics is not for them, and achieve a new confidence through the discovery that they can indeed function as mathematicians, whatever the lessons of their previous experience. If this happens they may want to test their growth by transferring their insights to mathematical areas that may require additional functionings. Two of these will be the subject of further books in this series: on geometry and on analysis.

Caleb Gattegno
New York City
August 1973

Part I
Actions Which Generate Numerals

1 The Set of One's Fingers

The content of this chapter is discussed from the point of view of the activity of a teacher and some children, but it would be as well for the reader to take some time looking at his own hands held in front of him, palms towards himself, following some of the activities described.

Since for most of us our fingers will obey instructions from our will, a preliminary game goes as follows.

Teacher: *Hold your hands in front of you with all the fingers stretched out. Now fold down your right index finger (or your left thumb, or both thumbs, etc.)**

* We will subsequently use the convenient verb forms 'fold' and 'unfold.'

Each time the teacher gives an instruction he folds the same fingers himself.

Teacher: *Do with your fingers exactly what I do with mine.*

He watches the students fold fingers corresponding to his. It does not matter whether they choose to make their left and right hands correspond to his, or whether they reverse them, provided the exact correspondence of fingers can be seen. This preliminary game is quickly mastered as the will can usually act immediately on the muscle tone of the fingers.*

The teacher then folds one or two fingers on one or both hands and asks the students to do what he has done. If they do this successfully, he folds an additional finger or fingers and asks them to do the same.

It may be interesting to readers at this stage to note that there are ten choices of showing only one finger, forty-five of showing only two fingers, one hundred and twenty of showing three, two hundred and ten of four, and two hundred and fifty-two of five. The order of these numbers is reversed for the number of ways

---

* Nevertheless the game can lead to some somatic awarenesses. Not all our fingers respond equally readily to our will; some people find some configurations extremely difficult to produce. Besides the possibility that this could lead to a useful physio-psychological test, the discovery of how little one owns one's soma may have consequences for one's self-education. Practicing these games may make some people less rigid, more supple in their soma and in their mind. Where configurations need a considerable effort for their production, the teacher may drop them for the purpose of moving ahead with the mathematical investigation. Not all configurations are required for this end; only the knowing that is produced by the activity.

of showing six, seven, eight or nine fingers. There is one way of showing no fingers and one way of showing all ten fingers. The following table demonstrates, at this stage of the game, the enormous variety of showings that are available.

number of fingers	0	1	2	3	4	5	6	7	8	9	10
number of choices	1	10	45	120	210	252	210	120	45	10	1

The table with its obvious richness may suggest to teachers how little they have exploited the set of fingers that everyone carries around with him every day. In particular it may suggest how they can show the classes of equivalent sets of fingers which exemplify what we call cardinal numbers. As well as this important awareness there is another still more important for our purpose. It concerns *complementary subsets*. Since each finger can be characterized as folded or unfolded, and the two states are mutually exclusive, any subset of unfolded fingers can be matched with another subset made by changing the state of each finger on both hands. The union of the two subsets is always the whole set of fingers.

To bring this out we may change the game.

Teacher: *Look at my hands. You can see some of my fingers but not all of them. (He turns his hands momentarily to show the folded fingers.) Will you unfold your fingers corresponding to my folded ones, and fold those corresponding to my unfolded ones?*

If the class clearly understands the instruction they can produce a very large number of configurations.

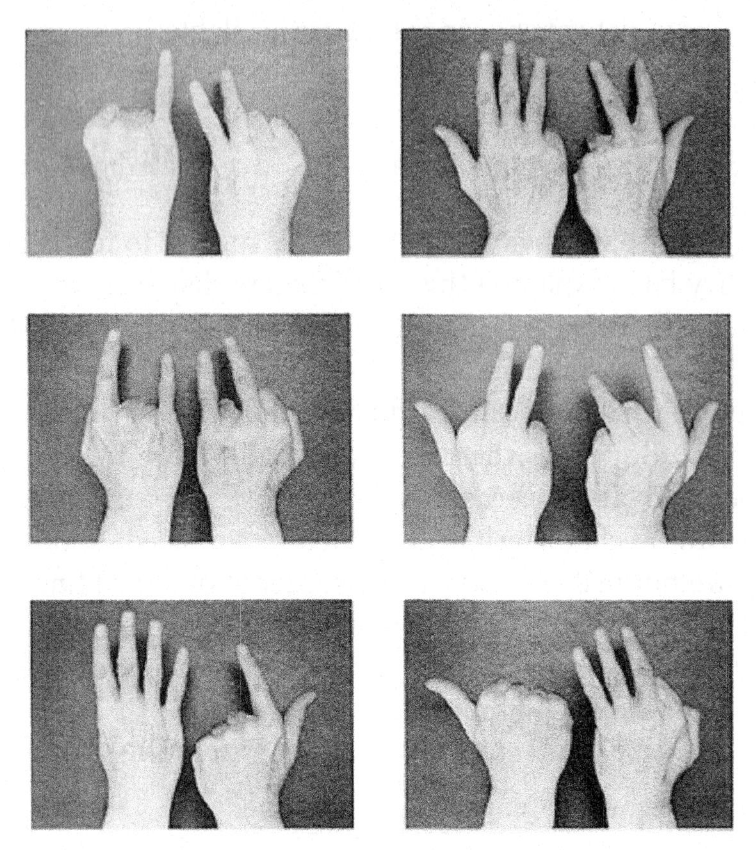

Three pairs of complementary subsets.

The game with the hands is fun as long as its demands on the students do not become too great. As we have noticed, some configurations are difficult to make, and the teacher can create a sense of relief at a certain moment by proposing a shift to a verbal system which is more restricted and easier to deal with. He can ask the students to call out the numeral describing the count of their unfolded fingers after he has told them his.

Clearly the 252 configurations of five unfolded fingers will now all be associated with the same sound. This is the restriction of the verbal system referred to above. The students experience the fact that a large variety of subsets will only trigger one sound, and if the teacher is sensitive to the importance of the association he will not hurry to stop his class from becoming deeply aware — by acting in the situation, not by being told about it — that the sounds for 1, 2, 3, 4, 5, 6, 7, 8, 9 describe many configurations. Each therefore applies to several different sets of fingers, although *zero* and *ten* in the present context each apply to only one set.

But the ease of uttering as against the difficulty of showing also permits awareness to be focused on the constancy of the pairing of the sounds — *two* with *eight* and *eight* with *two,* for example. A new opportunity has arisen for a new awareness.

Now the exercise becomes the recognition that it is possible to shift from one pair of sounds to another. By reversal, for example, (2,8) becomes (8,2). By folding or unfolding one or more fingers a given pair of sounds can be changed into another; the passage from (2,8) to (1,9) or (3,7) for example, comes from allowing one finger to pass from the subset of folded fingers into the subset of unfolded fingers, or vice-versa.

Students soon realize that the teacher is not necessary to the game and by looking at their own hands they are able simultaneously to see a pair of complementary subsets and to act upon it to produce either the same pair of numerals or a related pair.

Though there are so many configurations there are only a small number of pairs of sounds needed to describe them: (*zero, ten*), (*one, nine*), (*two, eight*), (*three, seven*), (*four, six*), (*five, five*). Exactly six if we are not interested in the order of the sounds; eleven if we are.

In the students' minds is now a wealth of experience of subsets of the set of fingers together with a move towards organizing it.*

In a similar way it is easy to find the subsets of the set of fingers when one of them, a thumb say, is taken out of circulation by folding it down and regarding it as immovable during the exercise. But it may not be necessary to do this. We shall see that an alternative route to the same results exists when we come to introduce the conventional numerals and replace a pair of sounds with a pair of signs.

If the students do not as yet own either the sounds or the signs of these numerals, a preliminary exercise will yield them. For this it is useful to obtain from the students a number of times the sound of each numeral simultaneously with showing an appropriate subset of fingers.

---

* For instance it can now be brought out that since the folding of some fingers produces at the same time a configuration of unfolded ones, there must be the same number of subsets for *two complementary cardinals*. Indeed, to show two fingers requires that eight have been folded, so to each choice of two particular fingers corresponds a particular choice of eight, and vice-versa. If we use the notation $\binom{10}{2}$ to indicate the number of different choices of two fingers from the whole set of ten fingers, then we can express this awareness by writing the following equivalences:
$\binom{10}{0} \sim \binom{10}{10}, \binom{10}{1} \sim \binom{10}{9}, \binom{10}{2} \sim \binom{10}{8}, \binom{10}{3} \sim \binom{10}{7}, \binom{10}{4} \sim \binom{10}{6}.$

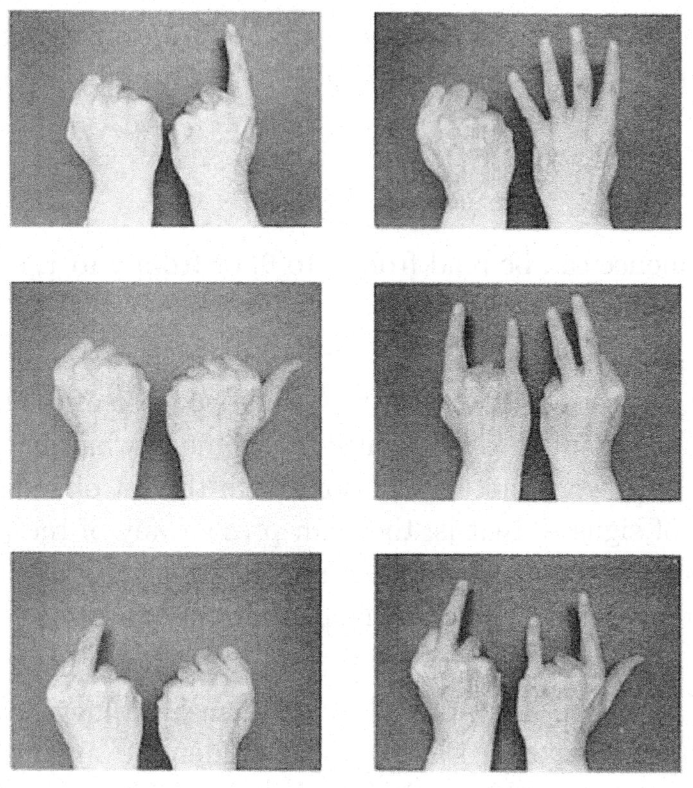

Alternative ways of showing *one* and *four*.

Not too far in the future this will become an instance of an important theorem in combinatorics, that

$$\binom{n}{p} \sim \binom{n}{n-p}$$

whose foundation can now be laid at the beginning of a mathematical education.

After the appropriate sound (*one, two,* etc.) has been uttered correctly several times for various subsets, the sign (1,2, etc.) is written up. As the ten numerals are produced *in any order* to match the correct showing of subsets of fingers, the following table of signs is built up:

1 2 3 4 5 6 7 8 9 (10)

The sequence can be read from 1 to 9, or from 9 to 1, or in any order.

It must be insisted upon that the whole purpose of the exercise is to give students the experience that some of what they can do with their fingers can also be done with the set of sounds and the set of signs — that is, they can present any of the possible subsets on their fingers, and therefore can also utter or show any one of the numerals which correspond to the subsets.

To return to the main thread of the game, we may now write (7,) on the chalkboard and ask the students if anyone knows what must be written in the blank space for the whole set of fingers to be accounted for. Since this is an exercise they have already practiced, there is little doubt that one or more students will answer *three* and that one or more will be able to enter 3 in the blank space. From this pair, (7,3) all the other pairs can be deduced and afterwards written up and uttered. With their eyes shut the students can now be asked to give the appropriate member of a pair when the teacher gives the other.

The crucial awareness here is that the folding of any one finger takes it out of the set represented by the numeral on one side of the comma and puts it into the set represented by the numeral on the other side. This transformation is so simple for most people to master and to become aware of that we can expect the students to learn that any pair can generate all others so that only one pair needs to be remembered by name. This is a measure of the cost to the memory of this mastery. One pair must be memorized but all pairs will be retained since none is more striking than another and, in fact, each one is capable of generating all of the others.

Once this material has been explored it is another very easy game to link the complementary pairs of numerals in nine to the complementary pairs in ten. The link can be made in two ways, first by finding the two sets of reversed pairs corresponding to any given pair of complements in ten. For instance, given the pair (4,6) one finger can be removed from either subset to give (3,6) or (4,5) and these pairs reversed to give (6,3) and (5,4). This can be done for each pair of complements in ten. Secondly, taking any pair of complements in nine, say (3,6) it can be used to deduce all the other pairs by folding or unfolding fingers in order to shift them from one subset to the other.

Of the eleven possible ways of writing complements in ten:

(0,10), (1,9), (2,8), (3,7), (4,6),

(5,5), (6,4), (7,3), (8,2), (9,1), (10,0),

we know that our indifference to the order of the two numerals reduces the list to only six:

(0,10), (1,9), (2,8), (3,7), (4,6), (5,5)

Similarly we may reduce the list of complements in nine to:

(0,9), (1,8), (2,7), (3,6), (4,5)

In fact our activities have established that any one of the pairs in either list can serve as the germ from which all the others in both lists can be generated.

It is clearly a possible development of the game that we may be tempted to make to consider what would happen if two fingers, both thumbs say, are regarded as fixed and immovable and to deduce the five pairs of complements in eight, utter them, and write them down as:

(0,8), (1,7), (2,6), (3,5), (4,4).

If this development is chosen and pursued through all the pairs down to (0,1) it is an advantage to articulate the total collection of pairs as fully as possible so that, for example, (2,) produces the correct response as a complement in ten, or nine, or eight, etc., given *in any order*. Whatever practice students have in this area will only be available to them for future use if all the articulations are working so that none is just a memory track but rather a link between numerals in specific circumstances defined by the name of the total set.

The collection of pairs may be written to give horizontally the set of complementary pairs in ten or nine, etc., and to give vertically the various complements to a particular numeral taken in different sets:

(0,10)	(1,9)	(2,8)	(3,7)	(4,6)	(5,5)
(0,9)	(1,8)	(2,7)	(3,6)	(4,5)	
(0,8)	(1,7)	(2,6)	(3,5)	(4,4)	
(0,7)	(1,6)	(2,5)	(3,4)		
(0,6)	(1,5)	(2,4)	(3,3)		
(0,5)	(1,4)	(2,3)			
(0,4)	(1,3)	(2,2)			
(0,3)	(1,2)				
(0,2)	(1,1)				
(0,1)					

The table shows that there are far fewer pairs to remember, even if all pairs had to be retained by drill, than shown in the usual lists of addition facts. Moreover we know that only one pair needs to be retained to make the whole table deducible through a process of folding or unfolding fingers in order to move horizontally, or of fixing or unfixing fingers in order to move vertically. But this is not the only direction in which development can take place. We know that a number of numerals in the English language trigger certain responses by their formation; for example, the termination:

— **ty** in *forty* or *sixty,* or the termination — **teen** in *fourteen* or *sixteen.*

It is easy therefore to introduce as *names* for sets of fingers *nine-ty* (when one thumb is fixed,) *eight-ty* (traditionally *eigh-ty) seven-ty, six-ty, for-ty,* and (as we accept the irregular spelling of *four-ty)* accept *five-ty, three-ty, two-ty* and *one-ty.* These are names for the cardinal of the set when the sound *-ty* is associated with the fingers while *one, two, three,* etc., have the same meaning as before. If we write *seven-ty* as 70 we can uniformly represent the *-ty* sound by 0. So we can write out a second line of our table:

1	2	3	4	5	6	7	8	9
10	20	30	40	50	60	70	80	90

We notice that *one-ty* had already been given another name, *ten.* It is at once obvious that if we play the game of complements on our fingers just as we did before, but this time putting *-ty* at the end of the naming of the numerals, we obtain, using the written signs,

(70,20), (50,40), (30,60), etc.

as pairs describing the complements in *nine-ty.*

If we happen to have followed the earlier development, described above as a temptation, we shall now have additional pairs such as (20,50) in the same line as (0,70) and be able to draw up a triangular table corresponding to the earlier one which will give all the complements ending in *-ty* in eighty, seventy, etc.

Ten-ty (which when written looks like 100, with a second zero after the one in 10) can be treated as we treated ten and we get (0,100), (10,90), (20,80), (30,70), (40,60), (50,50) as the set of pairs of *-ty* complements in *ten-ty.*

If we call *ten-ty one hundred, five-ty fifty, three-ty thirty* and *two-ty twenty,* we are back in the cultural fold and no one else need hear the unconventional sounds. But we have managed to obtain something remarkable at a very little cost. The game with the fingers can generate an indefinite set of pairs of complements by a mere change of the sound associated with the fingers. By uttering *hundred* after one, two, three, etc., and writing 00 for it after the signs 1, 2, 3, etc., we can know at once that (200,700) is a pair of complements in 900 because (2,7) is a pair of complements in 9.

Ten-hundred is called *one thousand* and it can be written 1000 since 10 is the written form for ten and 00 is the termination for hundred.

Similarly by calling each finger *thousand* we can form the pairs that are complementary in ten thousand and in nine thousand by using what we already know. Our knowledge can be extended to millions, billions, trillions, etc., just as easily.

What we have done so far is to use the insights provided by the game with the fingers to see how much of it is a matter of labeling and how much of it is an activity transferable to other numerals. What is transferable is the transformation effected by folding or unfolding fingers on the perception of a configuration of folded and unfolded fingers. Because each student can do this for himself, as a game played by his will with a concomitant awareness, the labeling appears as a simple and regular convention supplied from the out-side. In a very short time we have supplied the student with a vast net which has caught a multitude of relationships, easy to recall and remember, linked together, and with which we shall do a great deal in the next chapters.

One more game played with fingers can now be offered to the children. It will serve them well, but it needs to be done with care if it is to convey all the invaluable experience that can be found in it.

Let two students stand in front of the rest, facing them, with their hands raised so that they can be seen, palms towards themselves. The student on the left (from the watchers' point of view) "fixes" one of his thumbs. The teacher explains that the one able to use all his fingers calls them by no special name, but that the other calls them *-ty*. The two students show some fingers, folding the others.

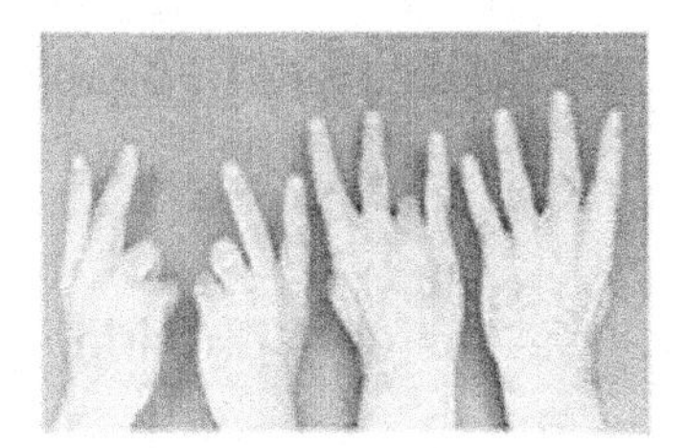
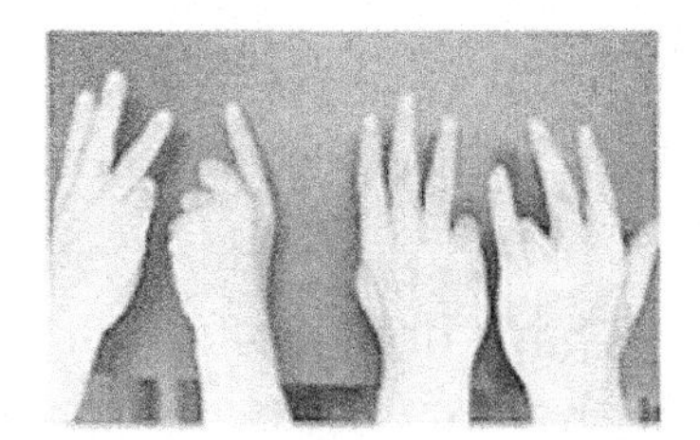

Two ways of showing *forty-seven*.

The other students read what they see, first reading the fingers of the student on the left, *for-ty;* then reading the fingers of the one on the right, *seven* say. Said quickly this sounds like *forty-seven.* The folded fingers, the ones not seen, can also be read. The sound heard will be *fifty-three.* The largest possible numeral that can be read, when all fingers are showing, is *ninety-ten* or one hundred. So forty-seven and fifty-three are complements in one hundred. After a few exercises of this kind it can be expected that the complement of any two-digit numeral in one hundred can be found.

A third student joins the other two on the left (that he is on the left is unseen by the class) and "fixes" one of his thumbs. His fingers are called *hundred.* The three students fold whichever fingers they choose and the class then reads from their left what can be seen, attaching *hundred* or *-ty* or nothing depending upon which student's fingers they are reading at the time. They may then read the unseen fingers, also from the left. For example, to *seven hundred forty-six* corresponds *two hundred fifty-four,* each is a complement of the other in one thousand. (The conventional 'and' that is usually spoken can be dealt with later, as can the irregularities in the *-ty* and *-teen* formations that have already been met.)

Any number of such examples can be worked out before the students are asked to say how they obtain complements in a hundred or a thousand (or ten thousand, one hundred thousand, etc., if more students are used in front of the class.) The students will be able to articulate this if only the teacher makes them note, in case it has escaped them, that all but one of the students have a thumb 'fixed' and that when this was done a few lessons earlier it was in order to provide the complements in nine.

The significance of this game is that the students acquire the procedure in their flesh; that they have experienced what part of the procedure is a generalization; and that they have seen that the usual notation of numerals is based on the fact that we add a new name when we move from one 'column' (a standing student) to the next.

But we cannot fail to notice that the only student with all his fingers free is the first and that this irregularity in the sequence must have some significance. Only the first student has the possibility of not only showing all the units of the first place (1, 2, 3, 4, 5, 6, 7, 8, 9) but of showing one of the second place as well (10). But if we modified the procedure by fixing a thumb of the first student and freeing the rest, we would not produce the traditional notation; and if we fixed a thumb on each student's hands we would not be able to show ten or hundred, etc. The traditional notation is a hybrid, as the irregularity demonstrates.*

This exploitation of a game with fingers shows how the students may learn how to *name* any numeral in the ordinary system; to *name* its complement in the smallest set whose written form

---

* It may be objected that this irregularity only emerges because we have tried to use sets of fingers to model the Hindu-Arabic numeration system and that it would not be a problem if we had used the model of 'bundling' objects in tens, hundreds, and so on. But this would then seem to attack the commonly-held view that the choice of base for our ordinary numeration system was a consequence of our having a particular set of fingers.

ends with as many zeros as there are students in the standing game; to *write* the numerals in the following table, and the pairs of complements in any of the numerals in the table (or the numerals in the left hand column, at least.)

Table growing from T_0 to T_3

1	2	3	4	5	6	7	8	9
10	20	30	40	50	60	70	80	90
100	200	300	400	500	600	700	800	900
1000	2000	3000	4000	5000	6000	7000	8000	9000

and so on.

2 Reading and Writing Numerals in any Base

The game with students described at the end of the first chapter led to a sequence of tables of numerals which need never come to an end. The extension of the sequence of tables is one way of exploiting to the full the knowledge obtained from the finger game. We will now show another way of looking at this accumulated experience in order to extend the students' awareness so that new fields or new ideas are offered to them as restructurations of that experience. In doing this we will be encouraging them to act as mathematicians and we can claim to be educating the mathematician in every child rather than giving them more material to assimilate.

First we see that notation in the ordinary system uses commas* in its written form to indicate thousands, millions (or thousands

---

* In the United Kingdom as in the rest of Europe spaces are now used instead of commas.

of thousands,) billions (or thousands of millions,) etc.* telling us that we could recast our earlier presentation by using a different device to lessen the burden on memory. We can therefore regard T_2 as the key.

T_2	1	2	3	4	5	6	7	8	9
	10	20	30	40	50	60	70	80	90
	100	200	300	400	500	600	700	800	900

With the table written on the chalkboard, and with a pointer to indicate the signs, the teacher can elicit from the students the *name* of any numeral up to 999. By touching not more than one sign in each line, and by moving from the bottom line to the top, he can expect them to respond by uttering the sounds they already know for each distinct sign in the table. In most cases if the sounds are made in quick succession they yield at once the usual sound of a numeral — *four hundred sixty-three,* for instance. In a relatively small number of cases the conventional sounds are formed irregularly and have to be learned. Some of these we have already discussed in chapter one; others that have to be known are *eleven, twelve, thirteen, fifteen* and the regular formations with *-teen.*

To obtain the written signs for these numerals we give a convention of writing in a vertical column starting from the

---

* This structure is also culturally specific. In East India, for instance, the traditional grouping is hundreds, hundreds of hundreds, etc.

bottom and dropping terminal zeros. Thus $\begin{matrix}3\\2\\8\end{matrix}$ is read, *eight hundred twenty-three.*

$\begin{matrix}4\\ \\7\end{matrix}$ is read *seven hundred four* while $\begin{matrix}4\\7\end{matrix}$ is read *seventy-four.*

A number of such vertical writings must be given to make sure that singularities like $\begin{matrix} \\ \\2\end{matrix}$ and $\begin{matrix}2\\ \\ \end{matrix}$, and say, 2 are read correctly, and can be written correctly when given in sounds by the teacher or another student.*

In order to pass from this vertical notation to the traditional horizontal notation we first of all deal with the three-figure numerals starting with those without a gap in any of the three possible places.

We agree, for example, to transform each triad according to the following schemas:

---

* In no case is it justified to read the numerals as a sequence of digits (as if one read the first example above as *eight two three.*) It may be all right to read a telephone or car registration numeral as a string of digits since no personality — or property except that of distinguishability — is attached to either. But a number has personality and 111, for example, is a very special entity, being equivalent to 3×37, in the ordinary system. It is essential, at least in the work discussed in this chapter, to give full names to all numerals since we are learning how to read and write them.

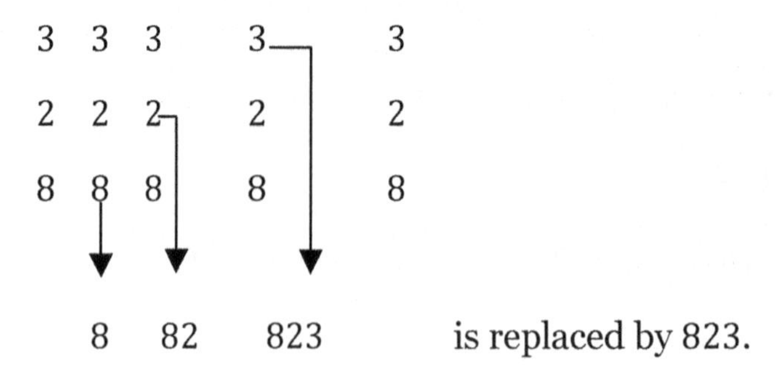

The teacher can use the pointer with the table to produce triads which are written first vertically and then horizontally by students. He can choose examples which demand closer and closer watchfulness if they are not to be confused.

2	8	1	4	4	5	
5	3	4	9	5	4	
7	9	6	5	9	9	etc.
752	938	641	594	954	945	

This is the first test on the way to mastery. The second comes when complete triads are now shown and only one or two signs are indicated. Vertically there is no ambiguity, but horizontally, unless the place of a digit is given by some indicator, there can be doubt. 2 may be 2 or 20 or 200.

The place holder zero may be best understood by starting with a numeral which does not use the second line of the table. We agree to place something to keep the other digits apart and 0 looks capable of doing just that. 603 says that 6 and 3 are not contiguous, whereas 63 says that they are.

Once a zero has occupied one empty space, two zeros can occupy two empty spaces. So 200, say, gains a new meaning. Earlier it was *twenty-ty*. Now it says: *There are two hundreds, no -ty's and no unnamed ones.* (The latter we shall call from now on units of zero order, either because they belong to T_0 or because there are *no* zeros in their written form. 27 has seven units of zero order and two units of the first order. The nomenclature can be practiced on a number of examples until it is thoroughly fluent. 453 has three units of zero order, five of the first order and four of the second.)

We will accept 002 or 012 or 020 as correct ways of writing numerals pointed out on T_2. In fact we shall need these formations when we write numerals such as one *thousand (and) two*. Later on we shall omit writing zeros if this does not create ambiguity and if we already have an agreed notation, as with 10, 20, etc.

We are now equipped to introduce the writing of any numeral.

We write in succession along a horizontal line a sequence of three-figure numerals:

453 772 564 822 934

If we rewrite 934 it can be easily read. We now place a comma to the left and then one figure to the left of that. That is, we write in rapid succession

934

,934

2,934

This can be read if the teacher gives the sound *thousand* to the comma, for the sound of the numeral will then be *two thousand nine hundred (and) thirty-four,* which is what anyone able to read numerals will say.

The next step is to place another digit on the left to produce say 22,934 which will be sounded *twenty-two thousand nine hundred (and) thirty-four*. Another digit, giving 822,934, will be sounded exactly as if it were composed of two numerals of three digits, the first being succeeded by the sound *thousand.* Taking other examples, each based on sets of three non-zero figures, we learn to read numerals of four, five or six figures.

Continuing the process for the next comma three places to the left of the first, and calling it *million,* we read 4,822,934; 64,822,934; 564,822,934; and any similar seven, eight or nine-figure numerals. By naming the commas further to the left *billion* and *trillion* we can now read numerals of up to fifteen digits.

Once this has been conquered we may go back to shorter numerals and consider what happens if zeros appear. Numerals such as 1,002; 40,008; 400,005; 2,000,007 are much more easily spoken given their written forms than written down from their names. In order to conquer the written form we may recognize that we have based our work on Table T_2 and limited ourselves to triads of figures. Let us accept this temporarily as a rule for *all* written forms so that when we hear a numeral which does not sound like a triad we know that a zero must appear somewhere in it. Some such numerals we are already familiar with; we regard *two hundred* as a single sound capable of being combined with other sounds, but when we hear it sounded alone we know its written form is 200. But we will use our new rule to cover a case like *twenty-three,* which we will write 023, where the 23 tells us what sound to make and the 0 merely makes it up to a three-digit sign. The zero has thus become a figure but it only has meaning within our written convention, so we will say that when it is at the left of a triad it is *non-significant.** When the written numeral is spoken the zero has no sound but can be represented by a deliberately observed silence. So, in the example 400,005, say, the 400 is sounded *four hundred,* the comma takes the sound *thousand,* and the last triad is given only the sound five; one of the zeros is for the silent *hundred* and the other for the silent *-ty.* Giving examples with one or two silences will provide the opportunity to practice this convention which harmonizes all possible cases.

Because we are concerned with establishing an exact correspondence between the sounds and the signs for numerals so that the students are able to pass without hesitation from one to the other, the teacher will find that the technique of dictation can play an important part in pinpointing the problems. A procedure that may be found helpful is for the teacher to start by

---

* If however another triad with some non-zero figures is placed on its left, the zero changes its role to that of placeholder and becomes significant.

dictating numerals and for the students to write solutions on the chalkboard, the remaining students being invited to approve or correct the results. Next the teacher can dictate while the students write their solutions on paper, exchanging papers to compare answers, the teacher intervening only when the students are completely lost, and only then by working a similar example on the chalkboard with the class as a whole. Finally students in pairs can dictate to each other and check their solutions in turn. The last phase gives the teacher the chance to observe whether mastery has been attained.

As an interlude in the reading and writing of Hindu-Arabic numerals, the Roman system can be introduced. This is not just a device to instruct the students in an historic but still-used notation; it is rather an occasion to consider and compare various inspirations directed at solving one particular problem and for evaluating what has been achieved so far. If we call the signs I, V, X by the names of the letters, by simple iteration of these sounds we can speak any of the following:

I	II	III	IV	V
VI	VII	VIII	IX	X
XI	XII	XIII	XIV	XV
XVI	XVII	XVIII	XIX	XX

It is clear that, if we interpret V as the set of fingers of one hand, X or X as the contents of two hands, and XV of three, etc., the system is consistent and reflects better than the Hindu-Arabic system the way one hand, then two hands, etc., are being looked at. Its drawbacks will not be in the area of notation.

We also notice that the above arrangement shows that it is possible to have a system that includes more than one notational base. If we continued with the Roman numerals, L would appear as another turning point in the notation, then C, then D, then M, and so on.

Examples of mixed bases other than the above form part of most systems of units of measurement. Clocks use seconds, minutes, hours and days that refer to base sixty, sixty and twenty-four.*

Base is the name given to the first point in a sequence of numerals at which a shift to a higher order takes place. On the common system, as it is arranged in T_3, T_4, etc. (see page 23,) each line has the same structure and starts as an iteration of ten, giving *ten-ty* on T_2, *ten (ten-ty)* on T_3, *ten (ten [ten-ty])* on T_4, etc.

We can generate the complete system of numerals by using the pointer in a systematic way: first on T0, then introducing 10 which enables 11, 12, 13, . . . 19 to be indicated, then introducing 20 which yields 21, 22, . . . 29, and so on up to 90 and 91-99, which is the explicit content of T1. This is followed by the introduction of 100 which can be associated with each combination already made to take us up to 199, then the introduction of 200, which will take us up to 299, and so on up to 999, which completes T_2.

---

* These systems are not 'pure' since although they use the idea of changing into units of a higher order they also use decimal numeration within each order; as in writing, for example, a time of 2 hours 32 minutes 54 seconds.

We shall assume that we have learned how to order the sequence of pointings on T_2 in such a way that the *recitation* of sounds from *one* to *nine hundred ninety nine* covers the same set of sounds in the same order as anyone would use. As we associate each utterance with showing a distinct and recognizable object (here this is the particular gesture of the pointer,) we have produced what we can legitimately call *counting*. The recitation of the proper sounds on its own does not constitute counting since we reserve this word to indicate that we have answered the question "how many?". This requires recitation together with a step-by-step passage from object to object in a set with the aim of exhausting the set without repetition or omission.

Finding a name for the base is a special problem which becomes very easy to solve when one looks at T_2; it is generally confused because of the irregularity that we have already noticed in the common system – that *ten* is the name for the full set of fingers of the first student in the finger game. Let us insert a vertical line on T_2 separating it into two parts, one containing the first column and the other not containing it.

1	2	3	4	5	6	7	8	9
10	20	30	40	50	60	70	80	90
100	200	300	400	500	600	700	800	900

The base for the set on the left in the illustration is 4, the first unit in T_0 which is not allowed in the set.

Hence there is no system with a base of 10 since 10 as we write it (and sound it) belongs to the second line of T_1, T_2, . . . , and *all* systems will contain it.* If we want to have a system with more than 9 units we have to widen it so that it contains the extra units. The letters of various alphabets will guarantee a sufficient supply of signs for most practical purposes. For instance, *A, B,* put after 9 give us what is called a *duodecimal system* and the extension of the next lines of T_2 by adding *A*0, *B*0, and *A*00, *B*00.

Once we are clear that the truncation or extension of T_2 gives a system of numeration in any base, all we have learned to do in the common system remains true for all the others. The difference lies only in the labeling of the sequence of numerals.

Thus in base 4 we may only use signs from the set on the left of the table on page 34. If we observe the agreed order we produce the following sequence:

> 1, 2, 3, 10, 11, 12, 13, 20, 21, 22, 23, 30, 31, 32, 33, 100, 101 and so on.

The sounds we give these numerals will be what we have already learned to use in the ordinary system of numeration which, for the mathematician, is not in any way privileged.

---

* Alternatively we can say that 10 is the sign and "ten" the sound for any base whatever. So it is still true that the base of the common system is 10, but now we see that when we are working in various bases we need some other system of signs to determine precisely which base we are to use.

In this chapter we are only concerned with reading and writing numerals. In the next chapters we will extend our powers and do much more with the elements that we have been able to single out and synthesize. So we will not study operations on numerals here but only note that what we have gathered so far permits us to ask questions like the following:

1. If we call alternate numerals *odd* or *even* according to whether their set includes 1 or not, what are the characteristics of these two sets in the various systems of numeration? (This can be put differently, and perhaps more provocatively, by asking, "When is 11, for example, an even number?")

2. Could 101 and 32 be the written results of counting the same set of objects in two different systems?

3. What are the complements in 100 of the following numerals, read as belonging to the systems whose bases are indicated by the Roman numerals?

   23 in (IV) (V) (VI) . . .(X)
   34 in (V) (VI) . . .(X)
   45 in (VI) . . .(X)
   56 in (VII) (VIII) (IX) (X)
   67 in (VIII) (IX) (X)
   78 in (IX) (X)
   89 in (X)

   Can you account for the answers? Can you find other numerals which behave similarly?

4 We will say that the numeral *A* *precedes* the numeral *B* in any system (and write $A < B$ or $B > A$) if in the ordered sequence of sounds starting with *one* the sound of *A* is heard before the sound of *B*. (For systems in any base between 2 and 9 – i.e. which use only those signs used in the common system-that is equivalent to saying that the sound of *A* is heard before the sound of *B* in the recitation of the common system.)

Which numeral immediately succeeds

$13^{(IV)}$ $24^{(V)}$ $111^{(II)}$ $344^{(V)}$ $555^{(VI)}$?

Which numeral immediately precedes

$100^{(III)}$ $1{,}000^{(IV)}$ $10{,}000^{(II)}$ $876^{(IX)}$ $300^{(IV)}$?

3 Exploiting Complementary Numerals

All the pairs of numerals that can be generated as complements within the same numeral in a particular numeration system will be called *equivalent.* So, for example, all the pairs we found in the common system in the first chapter, and all those we could have found in any base in the second chapter, which together form 10, or 100, or 1000, etc., are therefore equivalent. Since the pairs (3,7) and (6,4) can be found on the fingers of two hands, we shall write (3,7) ~ (6,4) and read this as, "the pairs three-seven and six-four are equivalent" or "the pair three-seven is equivalent to the pair six-four." This statement only links the two pairs, but since both are formed by partitioning the same set of fingers, we should be able to show this as well. We try:

$$(0,10) \sim (1,9) \sim (2,8) \sim (3,7) \sim (4,6) \sim (5,5)$$

The bringing together of all these observations still does not explicitly say that we are partitioning the same set. A more dynamic notation is needed. An arrow will perhaps serve this purpose; and, furthermore, the appearance of two numerals at one end of the arrow and one numeral at the other will indicate that two elements merge into one, or that one element is partitioned into two.

Adopting the traditional notation of addition to convey the notion of merging, say, 3 and 7 to form the set 10, we may write

$$3 + 7 \rightarrow 10 \qquad \text{or} \qquad 10 \rightarrow 3 + 7$$

An operation, which we are calling *addition,* and which displays the properties of activities with the fingers that we have already explored, must satisfy statements in this new notation that we have formerly acknowledged in the old. So we must be able to write, for instance,

$$3 + 7 \sim 7 + 3 \rightarrow 10$$

This indifference to the order of addition is usually referred to as the **commutative property** of addition.

We can use an arrow where we have previously used an equivalence sign since it is legitimate to think of having done something to the written form of a pair to make it look different from before:

$$3 + 7 \rightarrow 7 + 3 \rightarrow 10$$

Summing up our knowledge from the first chapter we may give the following statements as a sample of the many more that could be written:

$10 \rightarrow 1 + 9 \rightarrow 2 + 8 \rightarrow 3 + 7 \rightarrow 4 + 6 \rightarrow 5 + 5 \rightarrow 6 + 4 \rightarrow 7 + 3 \rightarrow 8 + 2 \rightarrow 9 + 1$

$100 \rightarrow 10 + 90 \rightarrow 20 + 80 \rightarrow 30 + 70 \rightarrow 40 + 60 \rightarrow 50 + 50 \rightarrow 60 + 40 \rightarrow 70 + 30 \rightarrow 80 + 20 \rightarrow 90 + 10$

$1000 \rightarrow 100 + 900 \rightarrow 200 + 800 \rightarrow$ etc.

In the common notational system that we are now using we can easily shift to the complements of numerals which lie between those mentioned above. For instance since 40 is the complement of 60 in 100, a numeral before or beyond 40 will be paired with a numeral beyond or before 60 respectively. In fact if we operate as follows the example can indicate how we can treat a number of cases so that the solution to the question, "what is the complement of such-and-such in such-and-such?" will be generally available.

Let us write any digit and immediately above it, its complement in 10. We put another digit on the immediate left of the first so that we have formed a numeral with units of both the zero and first orders. We add another digit above so that with the earlier complement it will now give us the complement in 100. We now put another digit on the left and form the complement of the new numeral in 1000, and so on.

2 (complement in 10) 52 (complement in 100)
8 48

652 (complement in 1000)
348

(It is instructive to compare this with a similar game in which successive digits are placed on the right instead of the left.)

What we have just done makes it easier to formalize what we have already learned from the finger game with the standing students. If we now introduce equivalent notations that we have already met together with a new one, we can practice writing them with numerals drawn from any table T_n.

$$(652,348) \sim (0,1000) \quad or \quad 652+348 \sim 1000 \quad or \quad \begin{array}{r} 652 \\ +348 \\ \hline 1000 \end{array}$$

What we want to do now is to reverse the relationships above and to call the finding of a complement the finding of the *difference* between, say, 1000 and 348 or 1000 and 652, and write it as a subtraction in either horizontal or vertical notation.

$$1000-348 \quad or \quad \begin{array}{r} 1000 \\ \underline{-348} \end{array} \quad ; \quad 1000-652 \quad or \quad \begin{array}{r} 1000 \\ \underline{-652} \end{array}$$

If we return to the fingers game, we can interpret folding as a disappearance, a *taking away,* and look at subtraction as taking 2 or 8 away from 10, or 348 or 652 away from 1000. All these expressions really mean, "find the complement," and if we are adept at this in any notation and using any equivalent form, we shall be less easily put off. So it is recommended that the students should meet exercises presented in a number of ways and for the language to be fixed only when it can trigger all the equivalent forms involved. A page of exercises might then look like this;

1 10 — 7 ~ ; 100 — 51 ~ ; 1,000 — 428 ~

2 Find the differences

100	1000	10,000
– 42	– 574	– 6,513

3 Put the complement where the arrow points

17 →(in 1,000) 35 →(in 100) 213→(in 10,000)

4 Put the following numerals in order as they appear in the sequence of counting numerals:

- complement of 528 in 1,000
- difference 1,000 — 491
- (3) 1000 – 617
- what is left when 373 is taken from 1,000
- the missing numeral in 742 + ___ = 1,000

The background experience that we can transfer from base to base we shall call the *algebra* of the situation. The ease of transfer from one base to another depends on an awareness that the algebra remains the same and that only the labels are necessarily different. Every time we find we have reached the way we operate in a situation we have reached the algebra in it, and this awareness enables us to distinguish, among the words used, those which refer to the inherent dynamics of the situation and those which are required because of its specificity. The two instructions,

find the complement of $11^{(IV)}$ in 100, and

find the complement of $11^{(V)}$ in 100,

refer to the same operations but necessarily yield different answers since there is a difference in the meaning of the numerals between one situation and the other.

Rather than make enormous efforts to avoid such situations because they could create confusion, teachers will be well advised, on the contrary, to use these situations systematically so that the students can disentangle the elements which cause the confusion.

The following game may also help in the disentangling of operations and labels.

Since the set of one's fingers is a datum that cannot be generally changed we will take it as an *absolute*. But on the other hand if we are gradually unfolding the fingers in order to label them, we know that any of them could be unfolded first and that any set of fingers could be labeled 10. Suppose we start from closed fists and unfold first the left thumb, saying *one* for it, then the adjacent index finger, saying *two,* then the adjacent middle finger, saying *ten.* If we follow the implications of this action, by saying to ourselves that we are only allowed to use 1 and 2 as units of zero order, we know that this corresponds to a vertical line being drawn on T_2 immediately to the right of 2, 20 and 200. So counting one's set of fingers can be understood as equivalent to counting with the numerals on the left of this line in T_2. The names of the fingers will therefore be 1, 2, 10, 11, 12, 20, 21, 22, 100, 101. We could reach the total in another way by counting the 10's, which would give 1 . . . 2 . . . 10, and since 10 tens is an equivalent expression for one hundred, and there is still one finger unaccounted for, the set of fingers can be labeled 101[(III.)]

Among the lessons that this game can teach us, apart from making the distinction between the set of fingers as an absolute and giving it a name which differs according to the labeling procedure used, we can note:

1 the numerals describing the whole set of fingers are not arbitrary; there are nine different possibilities because there are nine positions for the vertical line in T_2;

2 the smallest base is (II) (the corresponding system of numeration is called *binary;)*

3 in the binary system each of us has 10 hands;

4 the set of fingers could also be called 1111111111 in a system we might call "base I";

5 the set of fingers could never be labeled 15; why not?

Returning now to our treatment of subtraction we can look at the problem of finding the difference between two numerals by taking the complement of one in the other.

Since we already know how to find the complement of any numeral in another which has 1 as its first figure followed by as many zeros as there are digits in the given numeral, we can change a given pair of numerals into an equivalent pair by adding that complement to both and then finding the difference. For example, to find the difference between 71 and 48 we can add 29 to both and obtain an equivalent pair (100,77) where the difference is immediately seen as 23.

Let us make this explicit on a number of examples of subtraction which we shall work out in the common system.

The difference between 232 and 184, which can be written as:

$$232 - 184 \quad \text{or} \quad \begin{array}{r} 232 \\ -\ 184 \\ \hline \end{array} \quad \text{or even } (232,184)$$

will not change if we move 16 steps along the ordered set of the increasing numerals and replace both numerals by 248 and 200. We can then *hear* that the difference is 48. This we can write:

232 - 184 → 248 - 200 → 48

or

$$\begin{array}{r} 232 \\ -\underline{184} \end{array} \sim \begin{array}{r} 248 \\ -\underline{200} \\ 48 \end{array}$$

or (232,184) ~ (248,200) ~ (48,0.)

Another possibility would have been to find the complement of 184 in 200, or 16, and then add 32 to 16. The thinking could be illustrated by 232 −184 drawing a loop to indicate that we ask ourselves first what is the complement of the whole of the second numeral in the numeral 2, which is always read two hundred in that position; and this being 16 we can now add 16 and 32 to get the difference equivalent to the one asked for. A subtraction has been replaced by finding a complement followed by an addition.

Let us now consider a sequence of subtractions in which the length of the numerals and the bases vary.

A

$$\begin{array}{r} 11{,}213 \\ -\underline{6{,}758} \end{array}$$

In this, 11 has to be considered as 10 + 1 and the new form is clear;

$$\begin{array}{r} 11{,}213 \\ -\underline{6{,}758} \end{array}$$

the complement is 3,242 to be added to 1,213; answer: 4,455.

B

```
  101,202
 - 09,844
```

Similarly we write the complement of 09 thousand in 100 thousand (or 90,156.)

```
  101,202
 -09,844
```

to be added to 01,202, giving 91,358

C

```
  324,165
- 187,668
```

In this case the notation needs amental support for we can consider 3 as 2 + 1 and find the complement of 187,668 in the 200,000 (or 012,332) which we add to 124,165 that was left over. The answer is 136,497.

When we change base of numeration we operate exactly as above but remind ourselves that we no longer write 10 — 1 as 9 but as the last zero order unit in this system.

D In base (VI)

```
 123,203
 -44,344
```

```
 123,203
 -44,344
```

Again we consider the "loop" and write the complement of 44,344 in 100,000 in that base, (or 11,212) and add it to 23,203 getting 34,415.

E In base(II)

101,100,111
−10,111,010

101,100,111
−10,111,010

The "loop" tells us that the complement of 10,111,010 in 100,000,000, (or 01,000,101) is to be added to 01,100,111; *answer* 10,101,100.

F In base (XII)

402,133,408
−*AB*,98*A*,*BA*9

Since *B* ~ 10 — 1 in this system and 4 is 1 + 3 we find the complement of 0f *AB,98A,BA9* in 100,000,000 or 10,231,012 and add it to 02,133,408 and obtain 12,364,41*A*.

All these subtractions show that the finding of a complement is a routine operation and that every subtraction can be replaced by an addition. We can now consider how to use complements to speed up these additions.

We shall work first in the common base of numeration and give an example with four digits:

3678 + 5689 or in the vertical notation

$$\begin{array}{r} 3678 \\ +5689 \\ \hline \end{array}$$

Since we know that 311 is the complement of 689 in 1,000, we shift that amount from the top numeral to the bottom one and have $\begin{array}{r} 3367 \\ +6000 \\ \hline \end{array}$ and the answer is read immediately as 9367 and written from the left.

But we could also have noted that 322 is the complement of 678 in 1,000 and taken that amount from the bottom numeral to give it to the top one, or $\begin{array}{r} 4,000 \\ +5,367 \\ \hline \end{array}$ also immediately readable as 9367.

This transforming of the given operation in some examples which sound, look, and therefore are, easier to manage, will no doubt simplify the work on longer examples.

Because addition and subtraction *are* inverse operations it seems not only reasonable but in the nature of things to use them together as we did here to solve any problem which seems to contain only one of them.*

---

* Readers will have noticed that no word has been said about *carrying* in the transformation of addition proposed here. Indeed this operation only appears if we do not move towards using the artefact of the complements that generate zeros and thus eliminate the need for any addition. The only question that remains to be looked into refers to the case when it is not possible to shift the complement from one addend to the other. This is easily treated by generating zeros alternately or in sequence and then just reading the answer, as in the following example:

$$\begin{array}{r} 430,121 \\ +583,634 \\ \hline \end{array} \rightarrow \begin{array}{r} 410,055 \\ +603,700 \\ \hline \end{array} \text{ or } 1,013,755$$

In this approach (based essentially on complements,) we have not yet shifted from dealing with numerals to dealing with numbers since awareness of the properties of numerals is all we have needed to find the kind of answers we are after. Numerals are such well organized sets of sounds, or of written signs, that their use inevitably generates some meanings even though some other meanings which can also be carried by them are not yet made explicit.

The treatment of addition and subtraction of numerals in any base given in the preceding chapters makes it clear that we can perform these operations without the meaning that relates them to the coefficients of polynomials (see chapter 7, p. 66.)

4 Introducing One Aspect of Division

With the experience of numerals gained so far it proves possible to meet almost all the demands of "long division" defined as *repeated subtraction*. By showing that long division *can* be done without any prior knowledge of multiplication, we give readers the chance to compare this presentation with another, given in Gattegno Mathematics Book 2, and to determine which is epistemologically more sound.*

We already know how to subtract any numeral from another whatever number of digits they have and whatever the base that is used. So if we define division as repeated subtraction it is clear that we need only go on subtracting one numeral from the other as many times as it is possible to do so and then count up how many

* The alternative approach develops multiplication before division and is based on the use of Algebricks. Some such change of approach is eventually necessary since the method of complements is restricted to providing a model that is only adequate for the operations of addition and subtraction.

subtractions have been made. The subtracted numeral is called the *divisor,* the one it is subtracted from is the *dividend,* the number of times it is subtracted is called the *quotient,* and what is left of the dividend is called the *remainder.* The quotient therefore tells us how many times the divisor is contained in the dividend. We may write the operations in the traditional wav; for example:

$$\begin{array}{r} 2 \\ 3\overline{)6} \\ -3 \\ \hline 3 \\ -3 \\ \hline 0 \end{array}$$

says that it was possible to subtract 3 twice from 6 and that there was no remainder.

Clearly this example leads to an infinity of others if we merely put the same number of zeros after the 3 and the 6:

$$\begin{array}{rrrl} 2 & 2 & 2 & \\ 30\overline{)60} & 300\overline{)600} & 3000\overline{)6000} & \\ -30 & -300 & -3000 & \\ \hline 30 & 300 & 3000 & \textit{and so on} \\ -30 & -300 & -3000 & \\ \hline 0 & 0 & 0 & \end{array}$$

If we have 31 instead of 30 but keep the 60 as before, we have (where *r* indicates the remainder:)

```
     1 r 29
31)    60
      −31
       29
```

Had it been 29 instead of 30 we would have had:

```
      2 r 2
29)     60
       −29
        31
       −29
         2
```

So long as the number of subtractions is not large the procedure is tolerable but it becomes tedious long before the number of subtractions reaches the hundreds. It would not be a practicable method for finding, say, how many times 29 is contained in 15,358. But we can pause and ask ourselves if we know something that will enable us to economize on our efforts. Since *one hundred* is another name for *ten-ty, two hundred* for *twenty-ty, two hundred ninety* for *twenty-nine -ty,* we could subtract 290 each time and count 10 in the quotient for each subtraction. In this example it is even possible to subtract *(twenty-nine)-ty-ty,* or *twenty-nine hundred,* and count 100 in the quotient for each subtraction of 2900.

Each cluster of divisors that we subtract at one time we call a *partial quotient* and the total of the partial quotients is the actual quotient.

Treated in this way the example works out as follows:

	529 r 17
29) 15,358	
−2,900	100
12,458	
−2,900	100
9,558	
−2,900	100
6,658	
−2,900	100
3,758	
−2,900	100
858	
−290	10
568	
−290	10
278	
−29	1
249	
−29	1
220	
−29	1
191	
−29	1
162	

−29	1
133	
−29	1
104	
−29	1
75	
−29	1
46	
−29	1
17	

We could have saved some time in the last nine steps had we noticed that 278 is reasonably close to 290. So we could give 12 to the 278 and 10 times 29 again (giving a total to the partial quotients of 530.) Then to recoup what we gave we take one of the 29's (reducing the quotient to 529) and use it to supply the 12, leaving 29 — 12 or 17 as the remainder.

At a technical level we see that the kind of procedure we have just outlined enables us to tackle divisions, without any conscious prior acquaintance with multiples as a system, in any base of numeration and with numerals of any size. The procedure will, no doubt, in many cases be tedious to carry out; nevertheless it can be done. Whether it should be is, as we have already suggested, a question for the reader to answer. A reason for teaching it may well be that its clumsiness and tedium act as a motivation to students to become aware of ways in which the particularities of the examples enable the procedure to be compressed or re-organized. If this is so, teaching long division is to motivate students to become more alert to the characteristics of numerals, to be less clumsy and more imaginative. It may also have additional value in teaching what programming a computation requires.

Since any numeral can be composed of the numerals which can be found in one of the (T_n) tables, it will always be possible to perform a long division by using only what we have learned this far. Such exercises will contribute to an education of the student's flair and resourcefulness as he discovers that he can save himself much time by taking certain steps.

Looking at the number of digits in the dividend will show what is the largest number of zeros that can be put on the right of the divisor and still form a numeral that can be subtracted from the dividend. It will not be necessary to perform more than 10-1 such subtractions to reach a new dividend with at least one digit fewer than the original one.

Treating this dividend like the first we can again find that not more than 10-1 successive subtractions will reduce the number of digits in the dividend. And so on until a dividend with the same number of digits as the divisor is reached. This last division will never require more than 10-1 subtractions of the original divisor to produce a dividend smaller than the divisor. This last dividend will be the remainder. The quotient will be obtained by counting the successive partial quotients with the same number of zeros and reading the sequence as one numeral. As this study shows, this kind of long division can be carried out in any base since we have spoken of numerals, zeros and 10-1 only.

Part II
Actions Which Generate Algebra

5 A Model for the Algebra of Arithmetic

In modern mathematics the word *algebra* is used to mean a set together with an internal operation which associates to any pair of elements of the set another element of the same set. The set is then said to be *structured* by the operation. One and the same set can be the basis for more than one algebra if more operations are introduced. The different outcomes of the various operations are distinguished by being labeled differently. In this chapter we shall provide a number of algebras compatible with (i.e. which do not contradict) a set of rods with certain properties. This will make available models of algebraic structures so that the perception of what is done with the rods generates an awareness of operations on sets.

The set of rods we use is sometimes called Algebricks to suggest that their main purpose is to display algebra.

There is no intrinsically mathematical reason, only convenience, for choosing 1 sq. cm. prisms from 1 to 10 cm. long. The choice does indeed allow students to acquire spatial experience of the metric system and it permits a small amount of material to produce a considerable number of rods. This gives the illusion that the set of rods, though actually finite, is indefinite and can be conceived, by a leap of the imagination, as being infinite. Rods of one length are of one color, and conversely. This allows the quick recognition that they form classes of equivalence by length, and the separation into particular subsets that may be needed in certain circumstances.

Since the rods are of equal cross-section they can be assembled into trains of many lengths. The colors may suggest that we stress the segments, or we may regard a train as a whole.

The unifying characteristic of the rods is actually a concept, that of the length or volume of the rods. Whenever it will not create confusion we shall use the word *rod* for its length (or perhaps its volume; the context will tell.) A length can be perceived as a shift of awareness when one's eyes move from one extremity of a segment to the other.

It is in the succession of two movements of one's eyes when a train of two rods is scanned that we find the basic experience for the addition of lengths. (This is similar to the way in which we convince ourselves that two heaps of objects have been added.)

The psychological basis of algebra being the mental dynamic that makes us go from two things of a kind to one of the same kind, or vice-versa, we see that we can define *addition* as an operation upon the rods by putting any two of them end-to-end and substituting for the constituent pair of lengths the unique length separating the extremities of the train. That our eyes (and our touch, particularly in the case of blind people) also experience this merging of two lengths into one makes the awareness more apparent and the definition more easy to accept.

We are acting simultaneously at four levels:

1 the action of placing rods end-to-end,

2 the simultaneous perception of a train and of its components,

3 the recognition that there is a host of possible choices of pairs to put end-to-end,

4 the awareness that the sum is both generated by the train and distinct from it, and is only there if we will it to be.

Placing rods end-to-end is an action which carries an indifference with respect to the *order* in which they are placed end-to-end. This indifference becomes a property of the addition called **commutativity**.

If r and g are signs accepted as referring to a red and a green rod respectively, $r + g$ is in no way a better form than $g + r$. It is customary when one becomes aware of a property of an operation to state it explicitly and we call such a statement an *axiom.* So we now know that because of our initial indifference with respect to the order in which we place two rods end-to-end we can write:

1. $a + b \sim b + a$ ($\sim$ being read as "is equivalent to") to express the fact that the order of the rods is immaterial.

Note that we are also indifferent to the orientation or direction of the train in space.

Play with the rods very quickly yields the fact that trains can have more than two cars. To feel that here is a possibility that must be reconciled with the definition of addition as involving only two rods is to have become sensitive to the situation, critical of what one thinks and says, and determined to act (in this case) as a mathematician. It is obvious that in everyday language we can readily accept that a train is made of rods end-to-end although a third rod can only be end-to-end with one of the others and not both. If we experience this tension in the mind and yield to it to attempt to reconcile the words with the perception, we may discover that we have made some progress in awareness and are therefore better able to see further than before.

Indeed, if we ignore the rods and think only of their lengths, the operation of addition allows us to focus at one moment on the component lengths and at another on the single length that replaces the components. If we look at a train composed of three rods (lengths) we can also visualize it in two ways as composed of two lengths end-to-end, and thus as a situation falling under our definition of addition. Letting a, b, c represent the lengths of three rods, $(a + b)$ and $(b + c)$ can represent the perceptions of the single lengths equivalent to the lengths a and b or b and c end-to-end. Using this notation we can write about the train made of the lengths a,b,c that

$$(a + b) + c \sim a + (b + c)$$

since we can ignore the join between a and b or the join between b and c. Since we have now reconciled the existence of trains of three lengths with our definition of addition we can give ourselves the freedom to write the train as an addition even when the parentheses are removed. So we may say, as a *definition,* that $a + b + c$ is a new way of writing the above equivalence:

2. $a + b + c \sim (a + b) + c \sim a + (b + c.)$

The above definition describes a property of addition, called **associativity,** whose main function has been to raise the mind to a level from which it can preserve the validity of addition as an operation on only two elements and integrate trains of three lengths into the class of additions. As soon as we realize that the definition of addition is saved whilst its restriction has been opened up, we see that the role of the associative property is to put infinity within the reach of addition and make addition into a truly mathematical operation. From now on when we look at a set on which addition has been defined (as with the set of rods we are using as a model) we shall know:

1. that any pair of elements can be merged into (or mapped onto) a third, their sum;
2. that the act of adding another element to the pair is equivalent to adding it to their sum;
3. that this can be repeated indefinitely so that, although the sum can only be found for a finite number of elements, it can be extended again and again.

This precise examination of what is actually involved in our actions, in our thoughts, and in our perceptions, helps us to be "with" what we are doing and to claim exactly what we know and no more. In particular we see that the functioning of a mathematician is in fact the functioning of any mind with some polarization of attention on certain aspects of awareness, and not an awareness that only some specially gifted people enjoy. There is no more "abstraction" to the activity than when a two-year-old replaces meanings by words. There is no more "generalization" than in his use of nouns to refer to classes of objects.

We encountered a problem when we considered a train of three rods and it led to significant progress through our awareness of associativity. What advance may be experienced when we become aware that a train could have a single car? Is it really a train? Or can we make it a train by some new definition?

Indeed we can if we conceive of an imaginary car which can be paired with the given single car to form a train of two cars without affecting the length. This imaginary train we can call zero and write 0 for it.

3. $a + 0 \sim 0 + a \sim a$

summarizes what we have in mind. Zero is the length of a rod which when put end-to-end with any other rod forms a train whose length is that of the given rod. Although no such rods exist, our mind can produce as many as it wants and place each of them end-to-end with any other rod, including another zero rod.

Returning to our capacity to stress, for a train of two cars, either the lengths of the component cars, or of the whole train, or of both at the same time, we can ask ourselves whether the triplet a, b, $(a + b)$ can be handled to produce new awarenesses. Let us use c instead of $(a + b)$ to convey in another way that we are thinking of it as a whole. Then we may write $a + b \sim c$ and three variations of it arising from our indifference about the order of the equivalence (usually called *the symmetry of equivalence*) and about the order of the addition (commutativity):

$c \sim a + b$ $\qquad$ $b + a \sim c$ $\qquad$ $c \sim b + a$

If we omit the datum b and write a + □ ~ c, where the box sign indicates an omission and we call the form of the writing an *equation,* we can write three variations of it:

$c \sim a + \square$ $\qquad$ $\square + a \sim c$ $\qquad$ $c \sim \square + a$

and by omitting a or c instead of b *we can write another eight equations:*

$\square + b \sim c$	$b + \square \sim c$	$\square \sim a + b$	$\square \sim b + a$
$c \sim \square + b$	$c \sim b + \square$	$a + b \sim \square$	$b + a \sim \square$

All these variations represent awareness of some indifference made explicit.

All of these equations, thought of as relating to the rods, correspond to the existence of a gap in the triplet. But from another point of view what is at one moment a gap can be perceived as a difference in length. We will write $c - b$ to mean the difference between the lengths which we can interpret as that part of the length of (which is not covered up by b.) This gives us immediate access to alternative ways of writing some of the above equations:

$c - b \sim a$	$\square - b \sim a$	$c - \square \sim a$	$c - b \sim \square$
$a \sim c - b$	$a \sim \square - b$	$a \sim c - \square$	$\square \sim c - b$
$c - a \sim b$	$\square - a \sim b$	$c - a \sim \square$	$c - \square \sim b$
$b \sim c - a$	$b \sim \square - a$	$\square \sim c - a$	$b \sim c - \square$

We have shown that it is possible to construct thirty-two distinguishable statements for every triplet linked by addition and subtraction. This can offer students an awareness that given a simple relationship such as $a + b \sim c$ it is possible to transform it into 31 others. Specific "problems" can be characterized by the form that they transcribe into; the inner dynamics of the whole situation can then be used to change that one into any other in the set. When students have seen that one relationship enables them to think of many others that will do as well, they see that it is not necessary to memorize the 32 since each one mobilizes all the others, just as our thoughts immediately mobilize our speech and make it available for expression.

When we put two rods end-to-end we do not exclude the possibility that they may be the same color and the same length. Such a train displays *repeated addition* and since it is a special form of addition it will be possible to say things about it that do not apply to other kinds.

If two rods end-to-end are equal, when placed side-by-side they will form a rectangle. By focusing on this property we may differentiate repeated additions from other additions.

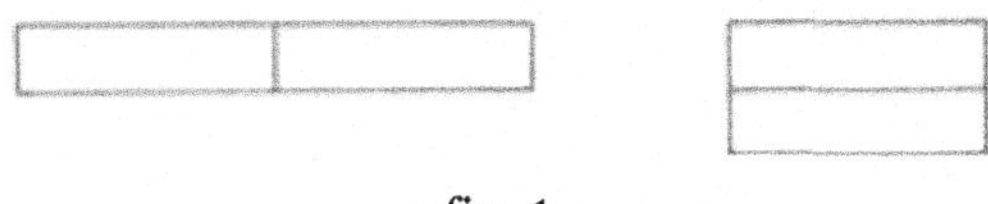

fig. 1

As soon as we have noticed that rectangles can be formed with equal rods we notice that it was only our propensity to stress some properties and ignore others at our convenience that made us stress length exclusively in the consideration of addition. In fact a train can also be seen to be a rectangle, with an area as well as a length, and the special case we are now considering has brought it to our attention because we have transformed this rectangle into an equivalent one. The simultaneous presence of the two attributes of length and area will be the key that we can use either to connect trains and rectangles or to distinguish them according to our needs. The set of rods can now serve as the model for a new operation which we shall call *multiplication* associated with the areas of rectangles.*

From a train made of rods of the same length we can obtain a rectangle both of whose dimensions are lengths of rods. In fact to each rectangle corresponds at least one other which is also made of rods of a single length and which can cover the first. (They are said to be congruent rectangles.) The two kinds of rods involved in the pair of rectangles have lengths which are equal respectively to the dimensions of either rectangle. When the rectangle is a square the two kinds of rods are equivalent.

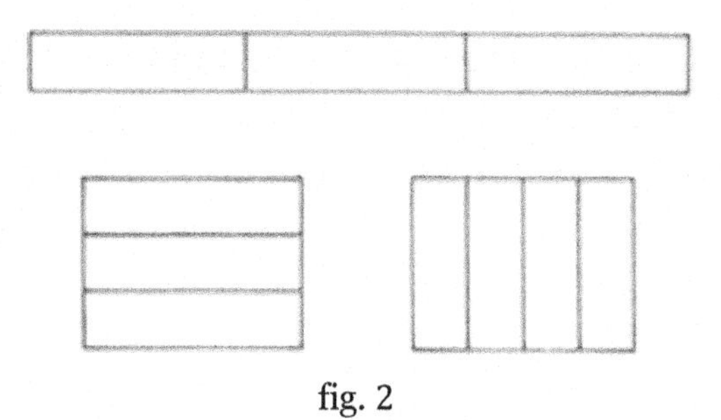

fig. 2

Let us economize in the use of rods by representing the pair of rectangles with one rod for each dimension, placing them so as to form a cross. Placing two rods in a cross in this way symbolizes a *product-two* products, in fact, depending on which rod is placed first. Our indifference to this order will allow us to speak of the *commutativity* of this operation of multiplication.

---

* We note that length and area are spatial or geometrical properties; the rods act as an *algebraic* model only when we put the stress on operating, changing, transforming, etc.

Here too we can break through the restriction implicit in the use of a pair in our definition of multiplication. A tower of three rods can be reduced to a cross in two ways, as shown in writing $(a \times b) \times c$ or $a \times (b \times c)$. Our indifference with respect to which alternative we take entitles us to define the two expressions as equivalent, which in turn allows us to write a tower without any parentheses at all: $a \times b \times c$. So multiplication is *associative.*

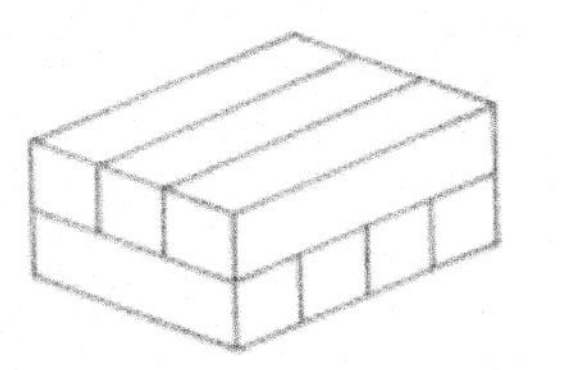

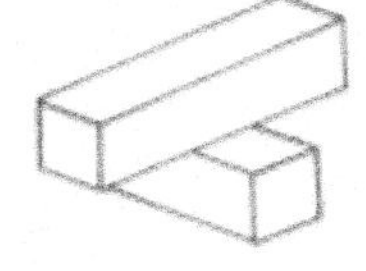

fig. 3

This is compatible with our model since we may substitute a train of rods for a cross made of two rods. Placing a third rod across gives either a cross in the first case or a tower of three rods in the other. These are therefore equivalent and the procedure shows how we may change a cross into a tower and vice-versa.

Multiplication therefore has the two properties:

(1) $a \times b \sim b \times a$

(2) $a \times (b \times c) \sim (a \times b) \times c \sim a \times b \times c$

and (2) can be extended to any number of *factors* or *divisors,* as the single components are called.

By making multiplication associative we have absorbed the set of crosses into the set of towers. If we now wish to integrate the "towers" of single rods into the set of towers, we can substitute for a single rod the "cross" made by placing a white rod on top. This cross suggests the definition of the *unit* or *identity* element for multiplication by saying that:

(3) $a \times 1 \sim 1 \times a \sim a.$

The similarity of the two structures of addition and multiplication is now complete.

We have two algebras defined on the rods-the algebra of addition defined for trains of rods, and the algebra of multiplication defined for towers of rods. A link between these two algebras is through a relationship called **the distributive law** or **the factoring** law depending on the direction of the relationship, in which multiplication and addition are considered and shown (in notation or with the rods) to be different.

Or in writing:

(4) $a \times (b + c) \sim a \times b + a \times c.$

Reading it from left to right, we can say we have *distributed a* over both *b* and *c*. Whereas if we read from right to left, we can say that we have taken a as a *common factor*.

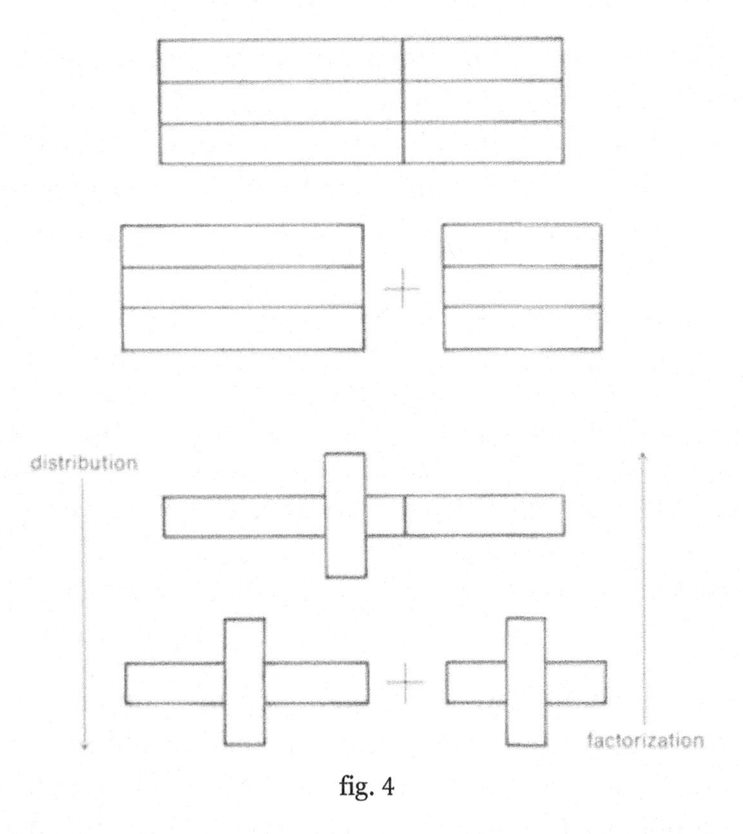

fig. 4

Another way to summarize (4) is to read the left hand side as saying “add first and then multiply” and the right as saying “multiply first and then add together”. The distributive law is the link between addition and multiplication regarded as *autonomous* operations. The fact that the operations were linked a *priori* (because multiplication was introduced as repeated addition) has not been used in the model in which trains and crosses are distinct and coexist.

Just as subtraction was introduced as the operation inverse to addition, *division* can be introduced as the operation inverse to

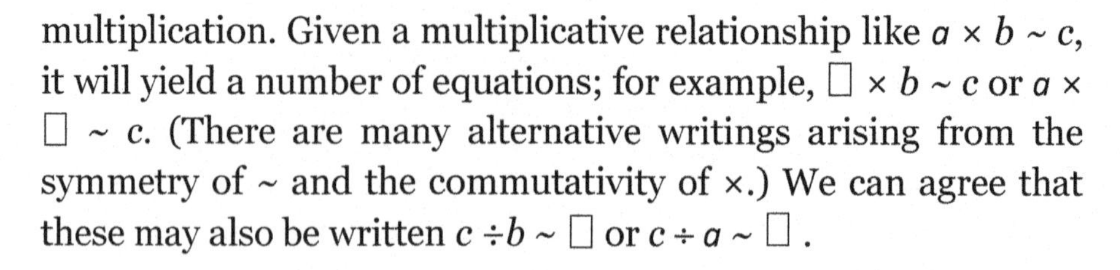

multiplication. Given a multiplicative relationship like $a \times b \sim c$, it will yield a number of equations; for example, $\square \times b \sim c$ or $a \times \square \sim c$. (There are many alternative writings arising from the symmetry of $\sim$ and the commutativity of $\times$.) We can agree that these may also be written $c \div b \sim \square$ or $c \div a \sim \square$.

We can also relate division to the awareness that if $a \times b \sim c$ then c can be obtained by the repeated addition of a *(b* times) or the repeated addition of *b* (*a* times.) So it will be possible to exhaust c by the repeated subtraction of *a* or of *b*. If *a* and *c* are both lengths, then *b* is a numeral saying how many times a *is contained in c* or *how many a's there are in c* or how many times a *goes into* c. We write $c \div a \sim b$ for this or, alternatively, $a\overline{)c}$ with b written above the c.

In an earlier chapter we operated a long division on numerals, asking how many times one numeral could be subtracted from another. The notation we used was similar to that used here. We note, though, that we cannot have a remainder in examples like those we have just encountered whereas we almost certainly will when we repeatedly subtract one numeral from another at random. Looking back we see that long division can be considered as the operation which yields the largest multiple of the divisor which is smaller than the dividend. This relates division to multiplication which, traditionally, it has always followed. We shall see in the next chapter that we can indeed speed up the process of finding the quotient in a long division when we know an adequate number of numerical products.

Nowhere in this chapter have we used the procedure of measuring rods to generate numerals. It has been shown to be possible to start with an awareness of algebra and to use the rods to exemplify operations on lengths or on areas before measurement is introduced. We can see, therefore, that it is not only possible to teach algebra before arithmetic but entirely reasonable to do so, since to obtain arithmetic we shall have to introduce the measurement of rods by each other and integrate this with all we already know about how rods relate to each other. The next chapter takes care of this development.

Part III
Numbers as Numerals Provided with an Algebra

6 Integers and Fractions

The Generation of Integers and Fractions

With a set of Algebricks we can form, and display all at once, all the different ways of making a particular length that the rods will allow. The way in which the rods are cut ensures that any length that can be made with rods (except the length made by a single white rod) can also be made in other ways. The set of all the ways of making a particular length with rods produces an *equivalence class:* all the trains in the set are equivalent since they have the same length. We will give the name *integer* to any such equivalence class. An integer will therefore have all the properties which are given by the construction of the class.

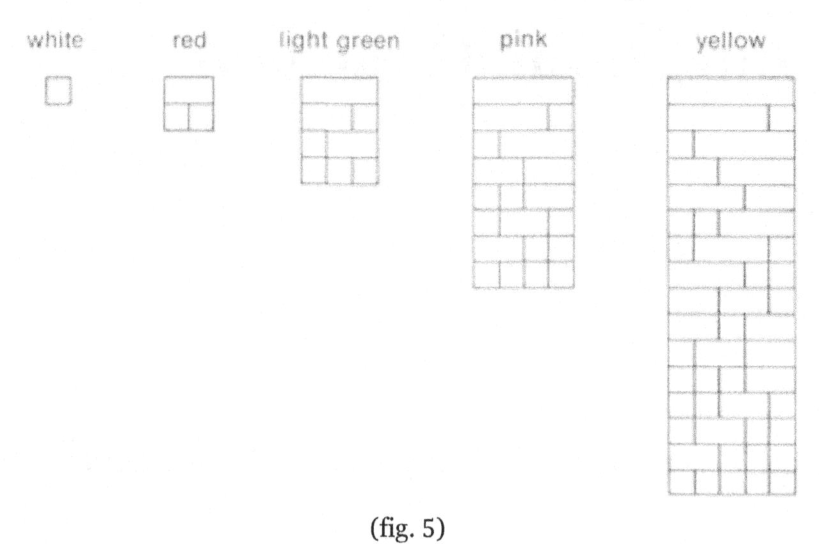

(fig. 5)

The figure on p. 51 shows some particular cases. We call each pattern of rods a *table of partitions.*

Since the length of each rod can be formed from a train of white rods each table will include a row of white rods. If we focus on this property we see that integers can be treated as part of a sequence of lengths comprising 1, 2, 3, . . . white rods. We have therefore linked the integers with numerals by looking at the white rows. But we can now notice that two successive integers differ by the same length, the length of a white rod, which can be taken to be a unit.

The integers can be named by counting the rows of white rods in any base, but to reach their other properties we must study the other rows of the tables.

Where one of the rows in a table is a single rod it is apparent that one entity can synthesize the integer. This understanding can be carried over to other cases, where the length of the rows is greater than the length of an orange rod, by a flight of the imagination.

Those rows in any table which are formed of just two rods will yield *complementary lengths* and hence provide another link with our work in the earlier chapters. We can study these rows as they appear in the various tables of partitions and notice that, by re-ordering the rows if necessary, we can produce a decreasing sequence of lengths at the left of each row and an increasing sequence of lengths at the right. The separation of the two sequences will produce "staircases" which can be re-united to generate a different length. This at once gives a vision of the link with the sets of complements as we have already encountered them (p. 9 and p. 24) and further reduces the burden on memory.

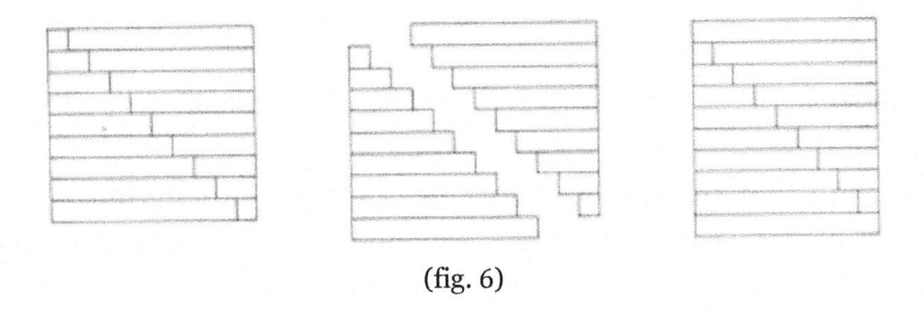

(fig. 6)

Nothing in the rods tells us that we have to call the white rod "one" so the same sets of complementary pairs can give us an infinite number of pairs of complementary numerals. For example, if the white rod is called successively "ten", "hundred", etc., the pair (7,3) can be re-named (70,30), (700,300), etc.

Studying staircases in their own right will give us an entry into *arithmetic progressions* — sequences of numbers such that the difference between one number and the next is constant. In particular we can once again discover the odd and even numbers by separating the rods into two sequences whose common difference is the length of a red rod.

Because we can link what we are now doing to our earlier experiences we see that we have at least two different models of the properties of the entities we first called numerals and are now calling integers. For instance, when we are naming the integers by counting the row of white rods, one, two . . ., we shall again meet the problem of which one to call "ten". In the present model because each length is perceived as an entity and because successive lengths differ by a white unit, any length, except the white one, can serve as a base and be called "ten". Suppose that we restrict ourselves to making lengths and white and red rods only, then we see that we can readily make trains of increasing length by following the pattern:

white; red; red and white; red and red; red and red and white;

etc., and that there is in theory no limit to the lengths we can construct. We can therefore, if we choose, decide to call the red rod "ten" and arrive at the successive numerals:

$$1;\ 10;\ 10+1 \sim 11;\ 10+10 \sim 100;\ 10+10+1 \sim 101;\ \text{etc.}$$

Similarly we could decide to call any other rod 10 and use the labels 1, 2, 3, . . . up to the length of the rod preceding the one we have decided to call 10.

We will not discuss the relation between the models in any more detail here. We only need to notice that we have not had to abandon anything we had already learned when we moved to the Algebricks model and that this new model enables us to see with our eyes what we had earlier perceived with our ears. The actions we described and formalized in the previous chapter will enable us to endow the integers with properties which were not so visible when we were working only at the level of numerals.

Returning to the tables of partitions, let us look at the rows we have not yet studied — those composed of 3, 4, 5, . . . rods. Consider the table of partitions based on the length of the dark green rod. Some of its rows contain exactly three rods: for example, three reds, or one white, one red and one light green. When we form these rows we can inspect them to see whether the same set of rods can be re-arranged to give any more distinguishable rows. The order (w,r,g) is only one of six possible arrangements of the same rods, the others being (w,g,r) (r,g,w) (r,w,g) (g,w,r) $(g,r,w.)$

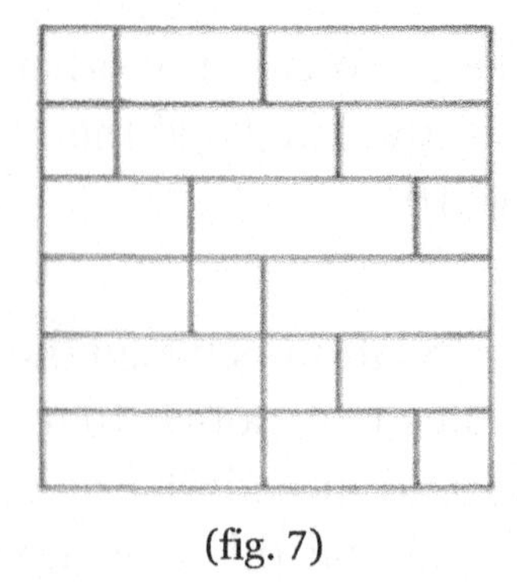

(fig. 7)

All six belong to the table of partitions of the dark green rod; we say they form the *set of permutations* of the white, red and light green rods. The other row containing three rods — three reds — will not yield any further arrangements since a change in the order of the rods will not lead to rows which are distinguishably different.

The table of partitions of the dark green rod also includes rows containing four rods; one of these is a row of two white and two red rods. In this case the colors of the rods are neither all different nor all the same.

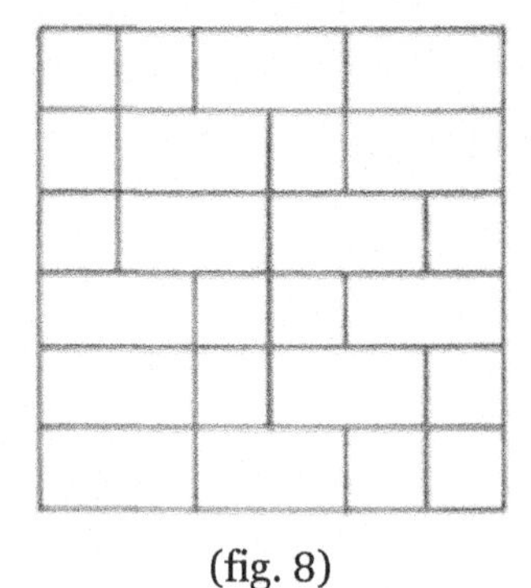

(fig. 8)

Working systematically in order to find all the permutations of a set of rods, which is necessary if the complete table of partitions is to be constructed, can teach us a great deal since we must develop criteria for generating the permutations, and they do not come at once to mind.

The completion of a few tables of partitions, which requires a good deal of the learner since they are so rich, gives experience which can lead to an astonishing amount of mathematics. An awareness of one's actions will produce the necessary generalizations — that is, the formalization of these actions independently of the particular objects which have been manipulated.

The activity of partition-making justifies the decision to call the classes of equivalent lengths *numbers,* and we see that particular numbers have all the properties which are simultaneously displayed by the complete table of partitions. Since the white row, which provides the numeral for a particular class, can be scattered on the table or piled in a heap, we can become aware that the number is associated with a *cardinal* — the cardinal of the set of rods in the white row. In this way trains can be transformed into sets, and although this is not a mathematical transformation it serves a mathematical awareness: anything we can do with sets can be mirrored by actions involving the white rows of the tables of partitions.

The reader will find in Appendix B a schema showing how many of the chapters of elementary mathematics can be generated from a study of partitions.

The next step we take has striking consequences, relating the world of integers to the world of fractions. It is based on the awareness that any rod can be used to measure, and therefore to name, any of the rows in the partitions.

If we measure rods with the white rod the names we obtain coincide with the numerals of the white rows in the appropriate tables of partitions. Thus the red rod is equivalent to 2 white rods, or $1r \sim 2w$; the light green is equivalent to 3 white rods, or $1g \sim 3w$; and so on.

If we now measure the white rod with other rods we need a new set of names. On the whole these names coincide with the *ordinals* — i.e. the names: *first, second, third, fourth, fifth,* etc. — except that one of these names is not needed and another is changed:

The white is called *one half* (not "one second") of the red;
one third of the light green;
one fourth of the pink;
one fifth of the yellow;
and so on.

The rule is very simple and the notation quite consistent. If a train X is equivalent to a train of, say, 19 white rods, then a white rod is called *one nineteenth* of X.

The notation X ~ 19w yields another form, w ~ $\frac{1}{19}$ × X, where × is read as "of." Hence $\frac{1}{2}, \frac{1}{3}, \frac{1}{4}, \frac{1}{5}$ . . . are the notations for the relationships which are the *inverses* of 2, 3, 4, 5, . . .

We can now proceed to the naming of any rod using any other rod as the measure. For example, to find the name of the black rod when measured by the brown rod, we only need to know:

1. that the name of a white rod measured by a brown rod is *one eighth,* written $\frac{1}{8}$; and
2. that there are 7 rods in the white train which is equivalent to a black rod.

Each rod being called one eighth, the name of the black will be *seven eighths.*

If we write (*b*,*t*) to mean that the black rod is measured with a brown (tan) rod, then we can also write:

$$(1 + 1 + 1+1+1 + 1+1,8) \quad \text{or } (7,8) \text{ or } \frac{7}{8}.$$

Let us note that as soon as we know the name of one rod measured by another we at once know the name for the reciprocal situation. For example, the name of the brown measured by the black, or (*t*,*b*) is $\frac{8}{7}$. This immediately provides a doubling of knowledge at no extra cost.

Pairs like $\frac{7}{8}$ and $\frac{8}{7}$ are called *reciprocal fractions.*

From the tables of partitions we can now obtain *equivalent expressions* for each rod measured by another. For example, considering the pair (5,7) and the table of partitions of the yellow rod, we have

$$\frac{5}{7} \sim \frac{4+1}{7} \sim \frac{3+2}{7} \sim \frac{2+2+1}{7} \sim \ldots$$

or

$$\frac{5}{7} \sim \frac{4}{7}+\frac{1}{7} \sim \frac{3}{7}+\frac{2}{7} \sim \frac{2}{7}+\frac{2}{7}+\frac{1}{7} \sim \ldots$$

We could also, of course, replace 7 by any of the 63 equivalent expressions obtained from the table of partitions of the black rod, but although possible this has no uses apart from bringing the awareness that complicated writings can be produced.

Other classes of equivalence are more useful. It is instructive to construct the classes that are obtained by measuring each rod by each of the other 9 rods in turn. Here is a part of the array that is obtained:

$$w \sim \frac{1}{2} \text{ x r} \sim \frac{1}{3} \text{ x g} \sim \frac{1}{4} \text{ x p} \sim \frac{1}{5} \text{ x y} \sim \quad \ldots\ldots\ldots$$

$$r \sim 2 \text{ x } w \sim \frac{2}{3} \text{ x } g \sim \frac{1}{2} \text{ x } p \sim \frac{2}{5} \text{ x } y \sim \quad \ldots\ldots\ldots$$

$$g \sim 3 \text{ x } w \sim \frac{3}{2} \text{ x } r \sim \frac{3}{4} \text{ x } p \sim \quad \ldots\ldots\ldots$$

$$p \sim 4 \text{ x } w \sim 2 \text{ x } r \sim \frac{4}{3} \text{ x } g \sim \qquad \ldots\ldots\ldots$$

In chapter 10 we make a different study of the set of fractions that arise from measuring one rod by another.

7 The Mathematics of Numbers

In this chapter we shall apply what we have learned so far to bring to life certain properties of numbers which have fascinated mankind for millennia in all parts of the world. We shall not follow a historical development, but instead gather together a number of properties that lead to a deeper acquaintance with numbers.

Up to this point we have mainly been concerned with the sequence of numbers, exemplified by the numerals we use for counting, and with the operations that can be performed on all numbers. These are two extreme positions: in the first we are concerned with what distinguishes any number from every other number — that is, that it occupies a unique position in the numerical order; in the second we are concerned with perfectly general ways of combining numbers to form other numbers — that is, we completely ignore the individuality of the particular numbers we operate on. In between these two positions is one which takes an interest in those attributes which are shared by some numbers but not by all; it is this position which leads to the study that mathematicians call *number theory.*

Although we have not deliberately gone in this direction so far, we can give two elementary examples which show how what we are going to do relates to what we have already done.

1 We look at the tables of partitions of numbers and notice that some contain a row of red rods only and that others do not. We can label the numbers *odd* or *even* if their respective partitions include a row of red rods with or without a white rod. This labeling then corresponds with the labeling of the numerals that we have already introduced.

   We can easily perceive that a general property (or theorem) concerning these numbers is: "When two numbers of the same parity are added the result is even, while it is odd if the parities differ."

   The proof is implicit in the fact that if two trains have only red rods, so has their sum, and that if both trains have red rods together with a white rod, the two whites can be replaced by another red rod.

2 If the table of partitions of a number contains at least one train made of rods of one color other than white, the number is called *composite.* Non-composite numbers, except 1, are called *prime,* and there are clearly many such numbers.

   As soon as this distinction is made we have new possibilities for grouping numbers, as well as the possibility of discovering properties that

> distinguish multiplicative and additive arithmetics. The number of partitions of an integer, which is an "additive" characteristic, increases as the number increases. But the expression of an integer as a product of primes, which is a multiplicative property, only requires its own prime factors, taken as many times as are necessary. It is a unique expression, completely characterizing the integer. Stressing the additive viewpoint distinguishes each integer from its successor, but the multiplicative viewpoint allows us to consider all integers together. The wealth of the additive viewpoint means extra difficulties; the relative poverty of the multiplicative approach makes generalization easier.

Through the many centuries in which men have studied numbers, the easier problems have been quickly exhausted, and we are left with a small number of problems which still tax the imaginations of the most talented mathematicians. Into the field of number theory only the most daring and hard-working mathematicians enter, and even they often have little to show.

In this book concerned with the teaching of elementary mathematics we shall restrict ourselves to the important and simple ideas — those which can be presented to elementary school students to improve their grasp of mathematics and their facility with numbers, and introduce them to the beauty and fascination of the properties of numbers.

1 Prime Factors

We have seen that a cross represents a product. All numbers which are prime can only be represented by a cross composed of a rod or a train across a white rod. The composite numbers, in general, can be represented by a cross whose elements do not necessarily represent primes. Each element which does not represent a prime can be replaced by a cross. By continuing to substitute a cross for a rod or train as often as it can be done, we finally arrive at a tower, each component of which represents a prime. This tower will be considered to be the unique representation of the composite number — that is, we will ignore the alternative arrangements of the composing rods.

For example, the tower for 72 can be obtained as follows:

The cross 2×36 yields a tower $2 \times 2 \times 18$, which yields $2 \times 2 \times 2 \times 9$, followed by $2 \times 2 \times 2 \times 3 \times 3$. This is a tower of primes that we can write shortly as $2^3 \times 3^2$ since it has 3 red rods on top of a green cross.

From this example, we can see that any composite number N whose prime factors can be called $a, b, c \ldots k$, say, can be represented by $N \sim a^\alpha \times b^\beta \times c^\gamma \ldots k^\kappa$ where the Greek letters represent the number of times the factor represented by the Latin letter is found in the tower.

This form for N expresses the "unicity theorem" we mentioned above. Only 72 is represented by $2^3 \times 3^2$; this form belongs to 72 and to no other number. From it we can conclude that 72 is divisible by 2, by 3, by 2^2, by 2×3, by 2^3, by 3^2, by $2^2 \times 3$, by 2×3^2, by $2^3 \times 3$, by $2^2 \times 3^2$ and by $2^3 \times 3^2$, since all these are seen to be factors of 72. (We do not include 1 since this is a factor of every number and so does not earn a place in a system of unique representations of numbers in terms of factors.)

Important facts follow from the possibility of such a form.

1 "If two numbers are divisible by the same number so are their sum and their difference."

Indeed, if $N_1 \sim a \times X$ and $N_2 \sim a \times Y$
then $N_1 + N_2 \sim (a \times X) + (a \times Y) \sim a \times (X + Y.)$
Similarly for $N_1 - N_2$.

2 *Corollary:* "If the sum of two numbers is divisible by a number which also divides one of the addends, it must divide the other."

3 "Two successive integers cannot have the same prime factors." For their difference 1 cannot be divided by any number besides 1.

4 We shall apply this last fact to obtain a celebrated and far reaching theorem, known as *Euclid's Theorem:* "The set of prime numbers is infinite."

Proof: we shall prove that to assume that there is a prime number P larger than all others will lead to a contradiction.

Let us call N the number obtained by adding 1 to the product of all the integers up to and including P. (We write $P!$ for this product.) i.e., $N \sim 1 \times 2 \times 3$

$\times 4 \times \ldots \times (P - 1) \times P + 1$ or $N \sim P!+1$. Either N is prime or not. If it is, since it is clearly larger than P, the assumption that P is the largest is proved false. If N is not prime it must have prime factors. If these were smaller than P, they would have to divide the difference $N - P!$, or 1, which is absurd. Hence N has prime factors larger than P, and this too contradicts the assumption that P is the largest prime.

That such questions can be asked so early in the study of numbers and require so little for their answer, although they refer to matters concerning infinity and make available a definite insight into the sequence of integers, is an indication of the power of the multiplicative theory of numbers.

2 Common Factors and Common Multiples

We now look at two other properties of numbers whose importance for further studies is considerable.

1 Let us make two different towers with prime lengths (i.e. rods or trains which are equivalent to a prime number of white rods) and let us form the set of their *common factors* by extracting from one tower all of the lengths or towers which are also contained in the other. These compose a tower which is contained in each of the two towers we began with.

For example $2^3 \times 3^2 \times 7$ (or 504) and $2^4 \times 3 \times 5^2$ (or 1200) have the following common factors: 2, 3, 2^2, 2×3, 2^3, $2^3 \times 3$. Of these $2^3 \times 3$ is the *highest common factor* or, in short, H.C.F.

The great German mathematician Gauss proposed the notation (N_1, N_2) for the H.C.F. of N_1 and N_2. Here $(504, 1200) \sim 24$.

2 A tower is called a *multiple* of another tower if it is identical with it, or if it contains within itself a tower identical with the other. Clearly there is an infinity of towers that are multiples of a given tower since placing more lengths in towers is always permissible.

If we give ourselves two towers N_1 and N_2, it is easy to produce a tower which is a *common multiple* of N_1 and N_2. It will contain within itself towers identical with N_1 and with N_2.

By starting with any one of these common multiples it may be possible to obtain another by removing a rod or a train from it. This process can only go on so long as every one of the prime factors of N_1 and N_2 remains in the *common multiple.* But each time we remove a factor which does not affect this property we reduce the common multiple tower. The lowest tower represents the *lowest common multiple,* or L.C.M., of N_1 and N_2. In Gauss' notation this is written $[N_1, N_2]$. For example, $[504, 1200] \sim 25{,}200$.

An elegant theorem, also due to Gauss, can be written

$$(N_1, N_2) \times [N_1, N_2] \sim N_1 \times N_2$$

or, in words, "The product of any two numbers is equal to the product of their H.C.F. and their L.C.M."

The proof with the towers of rods is illuminating. We leave it to readers to carry out on the above example, where the equivalence $24 \times 25{,}200 \sim 504 \times 1200$ verifies the statement, and to assure themselves that the demonstration is perfectly general.

To see that the words "highest" and "lowest" apply to two different sets of towers, and that although it is possible for the "highest" to be always smaller than the "lowest," this is only an apparent contradiction, will certainly help students in this area of mathematics.

To help further we can show two other properties.

1 For the H.C.F. and L.C.M. of two towers to be equal it is necessary that N_1 and N_2 be the same number;

  that is, if $(N_1, N_2) \sim [N_1, N_2]$
  then $N_1 \sim N_2$.
  Proof: (N_1, N_2) is a divisor of both N_1 *and* N_2.

  Since $[N_1, N_2]$ contains all the divisors of N_1 and/or N_2, the equality above implies that all divisors of N_1 and N_2 *are* divisors of N_1 or N_2, and that N_1 and N_2 have no divisor that is not owned by the other.

The unicity theorem then makes N_1 and N_2 identical.

2 The same phenomenon can be perceived when we ask a similar question about the sets common to two given sets, and the sets that simultaneously include these two given sets.

Let us consider two sets S_1 and S_2. If they have elements in common we can extract them one by one, two by two, etc., until we have taken all of them together. This procedure produces successive sets of common elements, the largest of which is the one containing all the common elements. This set is called the *intersection* of the given sets.

Clearly, unless S_1 and S_2 are chosen to make up the whole universe, there will be sets whose elements are all those of S_1 and all those of S_2 and of some others. By removing these others one by one, or in larger numbers, we form a succession of sets that contain the elements of S_1 and S_2, but each time with fewer and fewer elements not belonging to S_1 and S_2. In this sense these sets get progressively "smaller" and when all the extraneous elements are removed we arrive at the "smallest" set containing both S_1 and S_2. It is called the *union* of S_1 and S_2.

While to reach the intersection we widen the set of common elements, to reach the union we narrow the set encompassing them. They are movements in opposite directions – the "inner" sets are smaller than the "outer" ones, although the inner ones are expanding and the outer ones are shrinking.

3 Towers and Sets

The previous section dealt with two towers (or two sets.) It is obvious that we can consider any number of towers simultaneously and extend the definitions of H.C.F. and L.C.M. to any number of numbers.

Because multiplication is commutative and associative we can easily prove the following relationships (i.e. make sure that they actually hold:)

(1) $(N_1, N_2) \sim (N_2, N,)$

(2) $((N_1, N_2), N_3) \sim (N_1, (N_2, N_3).)$

Because of this latter property we can write (N_1, N_2, N_3) for the H.C.F. of three numbers. It follows that it can be extended to 4 numbers, then to 5, then to 6, etc., so that $(N_1, N_2, \ldots\ldots N_k)$ has a precise meaning.

We can of course, think up questions using this notation, like the following:

What is $((N_1, N_2), (N_2, N_3))$?

Is $(N_1, N_2) \sim (N_1^2\, N_2^2)$?

What more can be said?

Do we need to prove the same statements again when we replace the parentheses by brackets?

Can we mix these two kinds and ask questions about the results? For example, is

$$[(N_1, N_2), (N_2, N_3)] \sim ([N_1, N_2], [N_2, N_3])?$$

Can we construct and answer other questions of this kind? If it is easier to perceive relationships between sets in the algebra of intersection and union, can we translate our findings from that field to that of the theory of numbers?

Working with rods it is clear that we shift from one field *(set theory)* to the other *(number theory)* by building towers where before we had only scattered rods. If readers try this they will recognize not only how theorems are discovered but also how perception helps in the proof of mathematical propositions.*

4 Powers and Roots

Let us consider now a tower made of rods of one color. Let us choose red since there are more red rods in a box of Algebricks than, for example, blue ones.

---

* In my Books 5 & 7 (see bibliography) readers will find a number of questions which will illustrate this way of working.

This tower can be built up step by step and every time we place one more rod on the tower we can stop and speak about our actions and our perceptions using the language of multiplication.

For example, we can see that if r^6 (spoken "r to the sixth power") represents a tower of 6 red rods, r^6 can be divided by r, r^2, r^3, r^4 and r^5, with the respective results r^5, r^4, r^3, r^2 and r.

Hence $r^6 \sim r \times r^5 \sim r^2 \times r^4 \sim r^3 \times r^3$, or $r^6 \sim (r^3)^2$.

Also $r^6 \sim r^2 \times r^4 \sim r^2 \times (r^2 \times r^2) \sim r^2 \times r^2 \times r^2 \sim (r^2)^3$.

Again, $r^6 \div r^4 \sim r^2$, $r^6 \div r^2 \sim r^4$, etc.

If we know that the signs $\sqrt{}$ (called "square root,") $\sqrt[3]{}$ (called "cube root,") $\sqrt[4]{}$ (called "fourth root,") etc., indicate the operations which are the respective *inverses* of squaring, cubing, raising to the fourth power, etc. then other statements are immediately available.

For example: $\sqrt{r^6} \sim r^3$ and $\sqrt[3]{r^6} \sim r^2$.

We use the case of r^6 as an illustration of what is possible. Many more statements could have been made before we reached r^6, concerning r^5, r^4, r^3, r^2, relating them to each other in a number of ways.

For instance because $r^2 \sim \sqrt{r^4}$ and $r \sim \sqrt{r^2}$, we can write expressions like the following:

$r \sim \sqrt{\sqrt{r^4}} \sim \sqrt[3]{r^3}$.

The co-presence of many such statements in one's mind is a similar phenomenon to the grasp of a collection of synonyms.

Once it is understood that all we can say about the tower of red rods is also true for towers of any other rod, it becomes clear that we have met the algebra of *powers,* or the theory of *indices* or *exponents,* and of their inverses, the *roots.*

Three developments at once become possible.

1 The theory of polynomials.

2 The extension of the set of exponents to include negative and fractional ones.

3 A correspondence between multiplication and addition (and between division and subtraction) sometimes called the theory of *logarithms.*

1 Polynomials

Suppose we have a set of towers, each composed of repetitions of rods of the same color, but with different numbers of rods in each. Then we place any other rod across each tower. A *polynomial* is the name given to the form obtained by conceiving of the sum of all the products represented by the towers. The rod which is the basic constituent of each of the towers is called the *argument,* or *base,* of the polynomial, and the other rods are called *coefficients.*

For instance $A.t^n + B.t^{n-1} + \ldots + M.t^1 + N$ is a polynomial, in which $A, B \ldots M, N,$ are the coefficients and t is the argument, n is called the *degree* of the polynomial. We have systematically ordered the terms so that the exponents decrease from left to right. Sometimes the opposite order may be preferable, but even if the terms are not ordered at all the form is still that of a polynomial.

Numbers in the vulgar system *are read* as polynomials with ten as the argument and the numerals 0, 1, 2 . . . 9 as coefficients. The degree is calculable if we know that fen corresponds to degree 1, *hundred* to degree 2, *thousand* to degree 3 and *million* to degree 6, and that we can obtain any others by adding the degrees.

> For example, *seven million, three hundred and eighty-two thousand four hundred and fifty-six* (in figures 7,382,456) is read as if it were
>
> $7 \times 10^6 + (3 \times 10^2 + 8 \times 10 + 2) \times 10^3 + (4 \times 10^2 + 5 \times 10 + 6)$
>
> rather than
>
> $7 \times 10^6 + 3 \times 10^5 + 8 \times 10^4 + 2 \times 10^3 + 4 \times 10^2 + 5 \times 10 + 6$
>
> The degree of the polynomial is 6.

Every reader of this chapter has had a lot of experience with polynomials — in saying the names of numerals or in reading them. Numerals can be defined as the *matrix of the coefficients.* The matrix for the polynomial in the example above is 7382456. We see that the figures of a numeral only display the matrix, but that in speaking the numeral we reveal the underlying polynomial structure.

In the field of numerals it is a rule that no coefficient can exceed 10 — 1. All modern notation for numerals is decimal. What distinguishes one system from another is not the presence or absence of 10, but the name for 10 — 1. Hence if we know that in the common system (where 10 — 1 is called 9) we use polynomials for our calculations, we know that they are also available in all other systems of numeration.

The following three examples are not found in my books for students. They can help readers become quick at some multiplications in any system of numeration, and therefore in the common system, which is used in the illustration.

Examples

1 We can formulate rules for certain special products based on the behavior of these polynomials. For example, **The square of a number ending in 5 (common system) can be obtained by placing on the left of 25 the product of the coefficient of the 1st degree (the number of 10's) and that number plus one, e.g. 652 is obtained from 6 × 7 or 42, followed by 25, or 4225.**

Proof with the rods. (Although we use a geometrical demonstration here for its simplicity, we can still find the polynomial structure of the numerals in the way the lengths are composed.) We start with the representation of a number ending in 5, by taking a train made of orange rods followed on the right by a yellow one. To square this is to place trains identical to this one side by side until we get a square. This produces a large square containing at one corner a square made of 5 yellow rods, on the left of this square a rectangle made of orange rods, beneath the yellow square a yellow rectangle equal to the orange one, and finally an orange square.

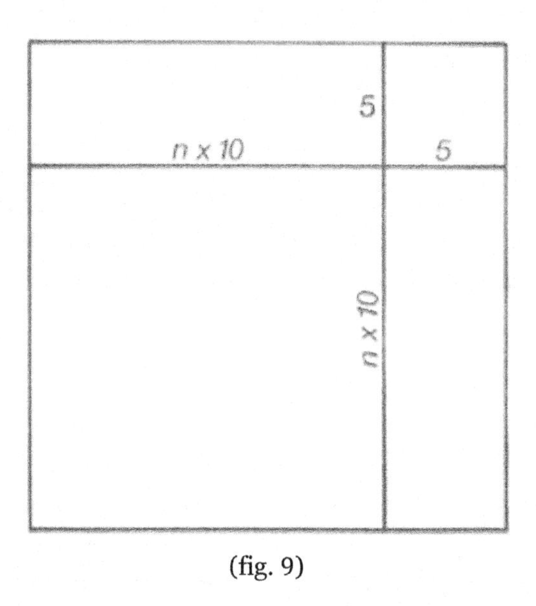

(fig. 9)

By moving the orange rectangle so as to put it side by side with the yellow one we generate a rectangle whose width is equal to the length of an orange rod. Hence we now have a yellow square (5 × 5) an orange square ($n \times 10 \times n \times 10$) and a rectangle (10 × n × 10.) The last two are multiples of 100, and there are $n^2 + n$, or $n \times (n + 1)$ such 100's. The two zeros of the hundreds make room for the digits of 25 and we have proved our proposition.

2 To multiply two numbers such as 66×64 we can apply the same dynamics. In the proof with the rods, instead of a yellow square we have a rectangle (6×4) at the top right corner. In place of $5 \times n \times 10 + 5 \times n \times 10$ put side by side to make $10 \times n \times 10$, we have $6 \times 60 + 4 \times 60$ to make 10×60, which added to the square 60×60 gives the rectangle 70×60.

In the same way as we did in the above example, we multiply 6×7, and write 42, followed by 6×4 or 24, i.e. 4,224, as the name for 66×64.

This awareness provides at once a *certain number* of products which look difficult to find mentally but are now reducible to two easy operations.

To compile the list we can see that by using the products of the complements in ten,

$1 \times 9 \sim 09$ $2 \times 8 \sim 16$ $3 \times 7 \sim 21$ $4 \times 6 \sim 24$ $5 \times 5 \sim 25$,

we know all of the following products:

$11 \times 19 \sim 209$ $12 \times 18 \sim 216$ $13 \times 17 \sim 221$
$21 \times 29 \sim 609$ $22 \times 28 \sim 616$ $23 \times 27 \sim 621$
$31 \times 39 \sim 1209$ $32 \times 38 \sim 1216$ $33 \times 37 \sim 1221$

$14 \times 16 \sim 224$ $15^2 \sim 225$
$24 \times 26 \sim 624$ $25^2 \sim 625$

$34 \times 36 \sim 1224 \qquad 35^2 \sim 1225 \qquad$ etc.

i.e. 45 products we no longer need to know by heart.

Note that many more products can be available because of other experiences the student has had. For instance, he knows 205^2 if he knows, or can quickly find, $2(0) \times 21$ or $21 \times 2(0)$. The product 42025 will then be so quickly obtained that it can be *seen* as the answer to 205^2. To do 335^2, he can multiply 33×34 easily if he knows that 33 is 3×11 and that to multiply 34 by 11 is to put $3 + 4$ or 7 between 3 and 4. He can multiply 374 by 3, obtaining 1122, follow it by 5×5 or 25, and get 112225 as the square of 335. An interesting property of 37 makes this mental calculation especially easy: $3 \times 37 \sim 111$. This property enables us to multiply 37 by any multiple of 3 up to 27 as easily as we can multiply by 111

$(37 \times 6 \sim 222; 37 \times 9 \sim 333; 37 \times 27 \sim 999)$

3 Another interesting but perhaps not very practical benefit of knowing about polynomials, is found in thinking of some numbers as polynomials in base 100 or 1,000. We shall use a mixed notation, the vulgar system giving the name and the writing, while we think of the number as arranged differently.

When we multiply polynomials we use the distributive law because polynomials are terms added to each other. Hence if we recall that $(a + b) \times c$ is replaceable by $a \times c + b \times c$, when c is itself a sum $(A + B)$ we have

$$(a + b) \times (A + B) \sim a \times (A + B) + b \times (A + B)$$
$$\sim a \times A + a \times B + b \times A + b \times B$$

giving us four terms in all.

This applies to such multiplications as

$$27 \times 34$$
$$\sim (20 + 7) \times (30 + 4)$$
$$\sim 20 \times 30 + 20 \times 4 + 7 \times 30 + 7 \times 4$$
$$\sim 600 + 80 + 210 + 28 \sim 918.$$

Now two numbers of three or four figures each can yield four products if we think of them as composed of so many hundreds and so many units. 1213 can be read $12 \times 100 + 13$. Let us multiply it by $11 \times 100 + 12$.

Using the above form:

$$1213 \times 1112$$
$$\sim 12 \times 100 \times 11 \times 100 + 12 \times 12 \times 100 + 13 \times 11 \times 100 + 12 \times 13.$$

The product on the left of the polynomial can be read as 12×11 hundred hundreds, the next two as $(12 \times 12 + 13 \times 11)$ hundreds. Hence if we can easily find 11×12, 12×12, 13×11 and 12×13, we can easily multiply mentally the two four-figure numbers.

In this case we know at once that 11 × 12 can be replaced by 132, 11 × 13 by 143, 12 × 12 by 144, and 13 × 12 by 144 + 12 or 156.

The written product, starting from the right, can be constructed in this way. Write 56 and carry one hundred; add 143 and 144 and 1, giving 288 hundred; write 88 on the left of 56 and carry 2 hundred hundreds; add this to 132 giving 134 hundred hundreds.

Hence 1213 × 1112 ~ 1,348,856.

As an example of a product in base 1000, let us take the square of 125,125. This is reducible since we know the square of 125 (125 × 125 or 15,625) to writing 625 and carrying 15; doubling 15625 before adding 15; hence writing 265 to the left of 625 and carrying 31, adding it to 15625.

Hence, $125{,}125^2$ ~ 15,656,265,625 — nice, even if not too practical.

Although to save time is important in life, such niceties cannot be justified today (except possibly for aesthetic reasons) as a necessary part of the elementary school curriculum. But for advanced students they can serve as a pointer to what *can* be attempted mentally as distinguished from what must be written or put into a machine or a computer. The fascination that has always been exerted by calculating prodigies clearly shows that men have appreciated the development of a specialized skill that goes far beyond mere usefulness.

It is interesting now to realize that all of us have been using polynomials implicitly while we were made to write and think in terms of the matrices of their coefficients.

2 Exponents

Towers made of rods of one color have a height that can be added to or subtracted from, and that can therefore serve as an "index" of what we are looking at.

Let us replace a tower of this kind by an **L** in which the horizontal part is a rod like the ones the tower is made of, and the vertical part is a rod that measures the height. Making a collection of such L's we can play some games that will yield new chapters of algebra and arithmetic.

When we look at any vertical rod we can see it as made of trains of smaller rods. We already know from the table of partitions that there are a finite and definite number of trains we can use to make such a height. For instance an **L** with a vertical dark green rod can be replaced by 31 different L's, the vertical trains being different either by their composition or the order of the coaches.

If we consider the **L** whose horizontal rod is orange and the vertical a dark green, we can obtain 32 alternative names for one million.

If the horizontal rod is red we can get 32 alternative names for 64.

That some of the names repeat themselves tells us something about the way the notation was invented and where to be careful when teaching it. For instance 10,000 and 10 × 1,000 must be distinguished. The L for 10,000 is made of a vertical pink rod and an horizontal orange rod, while the vertical in the L for 10 × 1000 is made of a white on top of a light green. Similarly 100,000 needs to be distinguished from 100 × 1,000. In speech, putting an s at the end of the name of the products 10 × 1000 and 100 × 1000 (*ten thousands* and *one hundred thousands*) will serve to distinguish them.

Let us make the set of L's representing the sequence of numbers

$10, 10^2, 10^3 \ldots 10^{10}, \ldots$
or $2, 2^2, 2^3 \ldots\ldots 2^{10}, \ldots.$
stopping where we wish.

It is easy to name each by the usual label. (For 10^6, say, a *million* or for 2^5, *thirty-two.)*

A number of relationships will become visible as soon as we use the tables of partitions for the vertical rods.

For instance, 2^{5+5} or 2^{10} can be written 32 × 32 or 32^2. Hence $1024 \sim 32^2$, which can be inverted to yield $32 \sim \sqrt{1024}$. From this we can obtain that $2 \sim \sqrt[5]{32} \sim \sqrt[5]{\ } \sqrt[2]{1024}$. From the sequence $4^3 \sim 8^2 \sim 64 \sim \sqrt{8192}$ we can extract $4 \sim \sqrt[3]{64} \sim \frac{1}{2} \times \sqrt{64} \sim \frac{1}{2} \sqrt{\ } \sqrt{8192}$.

Fractional Exponents

Playing the game of finding new names for any numeral suggests that we not only look at the vertical rods in relation to a single rod but that we introduce *fractional exponents* to describe one particular way of generating a new name. For instance, to generate the L of 16 from the L of 32 we replace the vertical yellow rod by the pink one. If we write $32^{\frac{4}{5}}$ to say which L we started with and what we then did to the vertical rod, we get a new notation which describes the action of pushing out the yellow rod and replacing it with the pink one.

That $32^{\frac{4}{5}}$ is equivalent to 16 is made visible, for we first *say* 32 but see 2^5 (an L) and that 2^4 is generated by the substitution of the pink for the yellow. 2^4 we see as an L but can *name* as 16.

As soon as fractional indices are introduced we have many new possibilities for writing the operations we have recorded before, and can therefore write relationships in new ways and read them easily.

$$\text{e.g. } 64^{\frac{1}{2}} \times 32^{\frac{2}{5}} \times 1024^{\frac{1}{10}}$$

$$\sim \sqrt{64} \times \left(\sqrt[5]{32}\right)^2 \times \sqrt[10]{1024}$$

$$\sim 8 \times 4 \times 2 \sim 64 \times 128^{\frac{6}{7}}$$

Mixing these notations we can write

$$\left(\sqrt{1024}\right)^{\frac{3}{5}} \times \left(\sqrt[3]{512}\right)^{\frac{4}{3}} \times \sqrt{(128)^{\frac{4}{7}}}$$

and work out the problems as easily as with integers.

Negative Exponents

Because we use rods on a table it may not occur to us to look at the possibility of turning L's upside down. Standing them on a mirror would do it easily, but holding an upside down L in one's hand may suggest it as well.

What do we learn when we become aware that ⌉ or ⌈ are possible arrangements and when we link them to what we have already done?

Where formerly we added rods to the vertical to make trains, we can subtract the lengths of rods from the vertical until the subtrahend is larger than the minuend and yields a "negative" vertical length. The notation explains itself, and 2^{-3} can be the ⌈ red, light green, obtained by dividing 2^5 by 2^8 (or 32 by 256) and named $\frac{7}{4}$.

We now have *negative exponents* to combine with fractional and integral exponents, numerals, roots and powers, and we can use them to invent any number of exercises. Numerous games suggest themselves and each student can choose his own examples.

Starting from something like $\frac{8}{32} \sim \frac{1}{4}$ we can write equivalent expressions which use all we have learned up to this point.

$$\frac{1}{4} \sim 4^{-1} \sim 2^{3} \times 2^{-5} \sim 2^{-2} \sim \left(\frac{1}{2}\right)^{2}, \text{ and so on.}$$

What is important is not the ability to find lots and lots of equivalent expressions, but rather that one is aware that they exist because it is a power of one's mind to perform transformations — at the verbal, notational and operational levels. In fact there are an infinite number of expressions for any one entity since combinations and permutations of combinations and permutations can be piled on each other. To be an educated mathematician is to find that the appropriate expression that relates to a given challenge comes to mind in the way words do. To strive towards this facility is part of one's mathematical education.

In the expanded study of exponents we have just carried out, notation as well as concepts grew out of an insight into the situation supplied by the shift from towers to L's. It proved adequate simply because the new notation blended so smoothly with all that preceded its introduction, and the extension of the concepts seemed so natural.

3 Logarithms

It will not take us long to notice that the exponential notation gives a mapping of one set of numbers into another and that while we multiply or divide numbers in the form of powers we only need to add or subtract the corresponding exponents. We discover that the correspondence between multiplication and addition and between division and subtraction generates a new extension of one's powers of calculation and therefore should be acquired in one's own interest.

To illustrate, once we develop and come to own the table of the powers of 2,

1	2	4	8	16	32	64	128	256	512	1024	2048	4096
2^0	2^1	2^2	2^3	2^4	2^5	2^6	2^7	2^8	2^9	2^{10}	2^{11}	2^{12}

we can obtain *at once* the answers to problems like the following where all that is required is a numerical name for an expression.

32^2 $\qquad 32^2 \sim (2^5)^2 \sim 2^{10} \sim$ **1024;**

64×32 $\qquad 64 \times 32 \sim 2^5 \times 2^5 \sim 2^{11} \sim$ **2048;**

$16^2 \times 4$ $\qquad 16^2 \times 4 \sim (2^4)^2 \times 2^2 \sim 2^5 \sim 2^2 \sim 2^{10} \sim$ **1024;**

$\frac{1}{32} \times 256$ $\qquad \frac{1}{32} \times 256 \sim 2^{-5} \times 2^8 \sim 2^{8-5} \sim 2^3 \sim$ **8**; and so on.

In these multiplications and divisions, we neither multiplied nor divided, but simply transformed the given expression to the point where the table provided the final reading. These calculations, like all others, are algebraic in character and need to be taught as such.

Logarithm is the name we give to the exponent when a certain number (or base) is raised to the power that makes it equivalent to another number. Thus the logarithm of 16 expressed to the base 2, is 4, or $\log_2 16 = 4$. We see that this is only an alternative description of the equivalence $16 \sim 2^4$, and that we are now calling "logarithm" what we formerly called "exponent."

An interesting exercise in the study of logarithms is the problem: "How much of the content of a logarithm table can be produced if we are given only the logarithms of two different numbers in the same base?"

Let us work it out in the case of the "common logarithms" — that is, those with base 10.

We already know that $\log_{10}10$ is another name for 1. Suppose we are told that $\log_{10}2 \sim .30103$ and $\log_{10}3 \sim .47711$. We can find the logarithms of the powers of 2, 3 and 10 by merely doubling and trebling the above logarithms.

$$\log 100 \sim \log 10^2 \sim 2 \times \log 10 \sim 2 \times 1 \sim \mathbf{2};$$

$$\log 8 \sim \log 2^3 \sim 3 \times \log 2 \sim 3 \times .30103 \sim \mathbf{.90309};$$

and, by similar methods, $\log 4 \sim \mathbf{.60206}$

$\log 9 \sim \mathbf{95422}$

$\log 81 \sim \mathbf{1.90844.}$

We can also find log 6 since $\log (2 \times 3) \sim \log 2 + \log 3 \sim \mathbf{.77814.}$

And $\log 12 \sim \log (2^2 \times 3) \sim 2 \times \log 2 + \log 3$

$\sim .60206 + .47711$

$\sim 1.07917.$

Calculations of some other values will employ subtraction and more complicated transformations.

$\log 5 \sim \log \frac{10}{2} \sim \log 10 - \log 2 \sim 1 - .30103 \sim \mathbf{.69897}$;

$\log 25 \sim \log (5^2) \sim 2 \times .69897 \sim \mathbf{1.39794}$;

$\log 72 \sim \log (2^3 \times 3^2) \sim 3 \times .30103 + 2 \times .47711 \sim$

$.90309 + .95422 \sim \mathbf{1.85731}$; and so on.

A table computed in this way shows that to fill the gaps of 7 and its multiples, 11 and its multiples (and so on, going through the prime numbers,) we will need to be told the common logarithms of the successive primes or shown how to find them independently. The second alternative is very complicated at this stage but we can see how we could proceed if log 7 is given and some gaps are filled, then log 11 is given and more gaps are filled, and so on.

It is now clear that we have put together a certain amount of mathematical experience that is important as mathematical "folklore" and that we can see how to teach only what is necessary, leaving the students to develop the rest independently.

In the case of logarithms we only need to know how to find those of the prime numbers. Indeed only 35 such logarithms need to be memorized to give the logarithms of all the integers up to 150. With them we could calculate mentally (with the degree of accuracy present in the estimation of these 35 logarithms) a vast number of complicated products, divisions, roots, etc. If we memorized these 35 logarithms and speeded up our additions and subtractions we could appear as calculating prodigies.

For instance, it would be possible to work out something like $\sqrt[9]{719}$ by replacing this particular challenge by others. We recognize that 719 is very near to 720, and that 720 ~ 8 × 9 × 10. The log of 720 can be found by additions, and the log of $\sqrt[9]{720}$ by taking $\frac{1}{9}$ of the result.

Log 720 can be found by adding 1 to log 72, already calculated above as 1.85731; $\frac{1}{9}$ of 2.85731 yields 0.31524 which tells us that $\sqrt[9]{719}$ falls between 2 and 2.5 (since log 25 ~ 1.39794, log 2.5 ~ .39794) but is much closer to 2 than 2.5. We suspect that it even falls between 2.1 and 2.2 (which we could check easily if we knew log 11.) This illustrates how far we can go without knowing by heart all the first 150 logarithms.

Though we need not expect such feats of everyone, and one can always buy a book of logarithm tables and do such calculations on paper, we still think that it is important to let teachers of elementary schools know that work of this kind can be undertaken by children of 8 or 9 if they are first allowed to make their own tables by calculating the logarithms of a few numbers. In this process they can discover the meaning of *approximation,* so that when we say, as we did above, that $\sqrt[9]{719}$ is a number between 2.1 and 2.2, the statement will make sense to them.

We have studied questions which belong to the folklore of mathematics for the reason that people learn music or poetry: to enjoy them and to feel one's mind expanded. A few of our students will choose to dedicate themselves to pure mathematics but all can entertain the questions of this chapter or those in a series of mathematics texts I have designed for students in elementary schools to use for independent study*. The level of difficulty does not go beyond what 8 to 11 year old students can easily handle. Books 5, 6 and 7 in this series contain further studies of numbers of the sort we have done here. In particular, polynomials are used to determine the transformation of numbers from one base of numeration into another, and approximation is studied and applied to the calculation of square roots and the calculus of errors.

The significance of what we have done here, and of what I have put in the text books, ties in the simultaneous consideration of the particularity of any problem encountered — so that we acquire the healthy trend of mind of letting each question guide us to its solution — and the ability to see what there is in the question that we have entertained that goes beyond its particularity.

This is what professional mathematicians do and this is what mathematical education is all about.

---

* See the bibliography on page 129.

Part IV
Teaching Mathematics

8 Teaching Mathematics to Teachers

Up to this point, readers of this book have been concerned with a new way of looking at mathematics through the awarenesses generated by the study of our set of fingers and of a model of algebra. Now we want to address ourselves to the people who teach mathematics and look more closely at what their job is. The teachers reading this book may ask, "How can we prepare ourselves as math teachers when we are so weak in our mathematical powers?" "Do we have to master mathematics in order to gather enough strength to be really helpful to our students?"

In this chapter teachers will find suggestions for bringing themselves and each other to a state of awareness which will make them more competent as calculators and more effective with their students. This state will not come about through the study of mathematical ideas alone. It is rather the ability to look with the eyes of mathematicians, to activate the powers each of us owns in common with mathematicians, that will help us most.

To bring readers to a point where they know the mathematician in themselves is for me a challenge of working on their awareness. Since I know that only awareness is educable, how can I see the challenge otherwise? It may follow that teachers who wish to reach others will find, as I have, that in order to do so one must first become aware of one's own awareness.

This subject of our study, mathematics, is a "science" which has been in existence for millennia. It has a history, and may be viewed as an edifice of accumulated results, ideas, theories and fashions. It is also an activity of the mind. It is probable that the nature of the activity has always been the same; a mathematician is a mathematician. But since throughout history the mathematicians were not asked, or did not volunteer to describe, what the activity of their minds was, it was left to the onlookers to understand it. These commentators saw very different things, depending on the place or time in which they lived.

Some of the work that historians of mathematics did was very worthwhile. They produced expositions of what some outstanding men and women had done over the centuries and were able to reach some conclusions. They saw, for example, that advances in the history of physics could be attributed to mathematicians having applied themselves to some models the physicists had produced.

The story of mathematics in the last few decades reveals that it has become an independent study, to a significant degree. The mathematicians of today work on mathematical challenges for their own sake. Structuring sets, setting axioms to link their elements in definite ways, and operating on them through the machinery of "the method," the mathematicians produce their works and publish them. No link with any other field is required for this.

What mathematicians of this school have not seen is that man's mind may function in such a way that he can study only those structures acceptable to it, that "the method" is perhaps the functioning of the brain. This being the case, mathematics always had its source in the awareness of what minds perceived in the outer or inner world. Today's mathematics is historically unique in that it focuses particularly on the workings of the inner world while continuing to pursue the impacts of the outer.

Our ability to look at human activity in terms of awareness and functionings gives us, the people of today, the ability to see new things and discover new hopes for the future. When teachers prepare themselves and work with each other in this new perspective, they will remain in contact with mathematics, with the mind, and with their students.

Among the many different functionings of man's mind we can see two which go to make the mathematician and these are the awarenesses, first, of *relationships* as such, and second, of the *dynamics of the mind* itself as it is involved in any functioning. Knowing this, teachers of mathematics can serve their students best by bringing them to the state of watchfulness in which they perceive how one becomes aware of relationships and of the dynamics of the mind.

We saw, in Part I, any two subsets of fingers of our hands as linked, and how the relationship of complementarity could become the basis of arithmetic. In Part II, we worked out our chapters by singling out relationships and exploring what followed from recognizing that a certain dynamics was linked to these relationships.

Looking at elementary mathematics in the way we did in Parts I and II has shown us that in fact very little *new* needs to be taught to teachers, and through them to the school population, for them all to own mathematics. From that small amount of new material much more can be generated through the use of our natural endowments, the powers of transformation and imagery that we use in speech. Therefore, in our way of working, to know a "little" brings about the consciousness of the "lot" that is implicit in that little when coupled with the generating dynamics the mind can provide. To know these powers of the self is to recognize what we have known all along (though we made no use of our knowledge when we saw that from a few words we could make many sentences.)

What we present to students of any age is what they cannot possibly find within themselves; these are the specific labels and notations whose exact forms are neither necessary nor held in common in all parts of the world. That we do not spontaneously understand speech in other tongues tells us that words have no meaning of their own and need to be associated with things we can perceive. Even words of one's own language that are not part of one's experience cannot be understood. Therefore it is the teacher's job to introduce to students the technical words of mathematics, words like "subtraction," "logarithm," "isomorphism," and the various notations, and make them clear through examples or definitions. *To teach* will be to find a way to make people mobilize some energy to hold on to these things that they cannot invent, and to integrate this energy through the dynamics of the self so that what has been held comes to function as part of one's whole self, in the way speech or actions do.

The most important lesson teachers can learn is that rather than teach mathematics we should strive to make people into mathematicians. That is to say, we should make people aware of certain powers they already possess which they can use in the same way that they are used by mathematicians. The professional mathematicians specialize in working on new challenges and publish their awarenesses; to a student, the challenge he is working on may seem just as new, though what he discovers may be already known. Since teachers should be more concerned with the dynamics of the mind as it functions in mathematical pursuits than in the novelty of the expression of an awareness, their preparation as mathematicians will be to become aware of particular functionings in themselves which they may later find to be educable in their students.

Specifically, the following points of focus will bring teachers closer to finding the mathematicians within themselves. Although they do not cover all the territory worth exploring, these touchstones alone, if carefully studied, will be sufficient to bring about a confidence and sense of direction in teachers which will allow them to continue their self-preparation on their own.

When teachers have completed the study of Parts I and II of this text, they are ready to reflect and become more deeply aware of what has happened to them. The bias we would like to develop in teachers is dual. On the one hand, we want to see them leave the atomic concept of knowing and see constellations linked to each other and explored as such, and on the other hand, to see that the dynamics of the mind can be at work in each item of a constellation as well as on the whole. Let us consider some examples:

1 Looking at the array (T_n) on page 42 we can see

- that the signs evoke specific sounds and these in turn specific signs, found in the top, middle or bottom rows according to how the sounds are formed (i.e. whether or not there is a suffix, and if there is, which one;)

- that 10 belongs to all systems of numeration; therefore we know that the difference between systems is in the units of the top row, one of them being replaced by ten (and giving its name to the base of numeration) and the ones after it being left out altogether;

- that the activities, which form the mathematics on the array, are independent of the base and therefore are learned once for all systems;

- that reading and writing numerals of any length in any base requires one and the same mastery;

- that these activities do not require:

1 that a unit be defined;

2 the awareness that one can do many things with these numerals which one day will generate an awareness of quantity.

2 Just as the array provides powerful examples of the linguistic functionings behind numeration and will make each teacher acknowledge at once the presence of power and experience in any student of any age who has already used speech, there are a number of other important awarenesses about the support speech gives in the study of mathematics.

We can see that *identity* is a very restrictive kind of relationship concerned with actual sameness, that *equality* points at an attribute which does not change, and that *equivalence* is concerned with a wider relationship where one agrees that for certain purposes it is possible to replace one item by another.

Equivalence being the most comprehensive relationship it will be also the most flexible, and therefore the most useful. In the field of everyday experience to state that "he is on my right" is equivalent to saying "I am on his left," and "I am taller than she" is equivalent to "she is shorter than I." So we all know that we say only one of the equivalent sentences and do not ever use both at the same time, and that one statement implies the other; we know that as soon as we choose who to refer to first, we must use a particular pronoun to govern the verb and another one to govern the object. This mental dynamics belongs to mathematics as well, because we use language to describe *all* activities, including mathematics. So if we say that 4 + 1 is the *same* as 5, or vice-versa, we cannot be correct. We must say instead that 4 + 1 and 5 are two *descriptions,* two *names* for a given set. Using language in this way, in mathematics classes, will give us greater precision and at the same time, greater freedom.

Another important awareness that a closer study of the use of language will bring to teachers is that there is so much algebra in the way their own minds handle the universe of words. Becoming sensitive to one's power to make different words out of the limited number of basic sounds of his own language, or to record those words in writing with an even more limited number of signs, one finds that one already has access to permutations and combinations.

An awareness of what words cover will yield classes (for nouns,) structuration of classes into sub-classes by attributes, and the algebra of classes as reflected by adjectives (which can yield Venn diagrams.) Other algebraic structures such as groups, rings and fields will be seen as elementary when compared to the complex structures used in making sentences and statements, which are accessible to all children in all environments very early in life. Relating mathematics to language, we will see that it has the same essence as the meanings behind words. As such, mathematics will generate new awarenesses through a dynamic like the one at work in speech when meanings generate sequences of words.

For example, to calculate

$$\frac{\sqrt[9]{512} \times \sqrt[3]{64^2}}{\sqrt[1]{16,384} \times \sqrt[11]{2048^3}} + \frac{\sqrt{1024} \times \sqrt[5]{32}}{\sqrt[15]{256 \times 128}}$$

is now simply a linguistic exercise within the algebras that govern numbers, known as powers of 2 in the decimal system, and including the various roots as inverses of powers. If we replace each term by the other name appropriate to this challenge, we read

$$\frac{2 \times 16}{4 \times 8} + \frac{32 \times 2}{2}$$

or $1 + 32$

or 33.

The calculation, then, is really a translation of a statement given in the language of powers and roots into one in the language of ordinary fractions, and a reading of the fractions with the understanding that the operations order us to rename them as integers where we can.

3 No problem in life is truly a problem unless it requires that we search for its solution. This generally requires that we transform the original challenge into others that can be more easily tackled. For example, lacking enough money to buy a house one has one problem which is quickly replaced by, "Where does one obtain money and on what terms?" The solution of the second problem is equivalent to a solution of the first.

In the meeting of mathematical problems we function in a similar manner. We transform the data to perceive a solution. Therefore to educate the mathematician in every teacher we invite him to work only on the procedure in order to find as many ways as he can to solve a problem, rather than to focus on the answer. A true spirit of yielding to problems brings about the emergence in one's mind of a wealth of alternative routes. The teacher who works in this way will find that he has more initiative himself and at the same time more confidence and peace with respect to the workings of his students' minds.

With this approach it is easier for students to realize that the form in which a problem is given by their teacher, or printed in a book, is not necessarily unique. Nor will they think that someone's way of solving a certain kind of problem is better than all others. Each solution may be stamped uniquely by the uniqueness of the solver.

Students and teachers alike will have new ways of evaluating solutions to problems. Some can be called economical, some elegant, brilliant or far-fetched, some awkward, clumsy, long or tortuous, although all are correct and mathematically acceptable. Part of a teacher's preparation as a mathematician will be to cultivate a sense of all these distinctions.

4 If teachers, many of whom have thought of themselves for years as slow and clumsy at computation, can make themselves quick calculators, they may delight in this metamorphosis of themselves and find it an inspiration in their work with their students. The key to quick calculation is the understanding that all operations are algebraic even when figures and digits appear. To calculate well is to have strings of forms equivalent to each other triggered instantly by a given problem which work like a chain reaction until they have brought the original statement to a form whose reading is the expected or required answer.

For example, consider the equivalent forms generated by the following situation. A square of pink rods is placed on top of a square of blue rods in the corner. The uncovered L-shaped blue area is the difference between the two squares. With the white rod as unit we can write this difference $9^2 - 4^2$. By moving the blue rods that are not covered by pink rods and turning them through a right angle, they can be replaced so that the blue area is transformed into a rectangle. Inspecting this rectangle we see that its length is the sum of the lengths of a blue rod and a pink rod, and that its width is the difference between these lengths. The area can be written $(9 + 4) \times (9 - 4)$. Therefore we have an equivalence, $9^2 - 4^2 \sim (9 + 4) \times (9 - 4)$.

By taking further instances we find that nothing in the algebra of this equivalence depends on the particular choice of rods. This generalization can be summarized by writing

$$a^2 - b^2 \sim (a + b) \times (a - b)$$

where a and b are integers and the only restriction is that a must be greater than b.

If this equivalence is part of our stock-in-trade it can be triggered whenever a suitable question appears. So the need to calculate $13^2 - 8^2$, say, will trigger $(13 + 8) \times (13 - 8)$ which will in turn trigger other equivalences until 105 is reached. But we may also turn to it in less obvious instances. For example, 99^2 may trigger $(99 + 1) \times (99 - 1) + 1^2$, which will trigger $100 \times 98 + 1$, which will trigger $9800 + 1$, or 9801; and 37×43 may trigger the pattern $(40 - 3) \times (40 + 3)$ which in turn triggers $40^2 - 3^2$, which asks for $(4 \times 10)^2 - 3^2$, or $16 \times 100 - 3^2$, which triggers $1600 - 9$, or $1600 - 10 + 1$, or 1591.

We saw earlier that the square of numbers ending in 5 (in the decimal system) can be calculated through a simplified algorithm which applies to the product of two numbers whose units are complementary in ten and whose other figures are identical. (See Chapter 7, page 106.) This clusters 65^2 with 64×66, 63×67, 62×68, 61×69. Remembering one pattern, we reap rewards in the many situations which have its particular attributes. The work with the rods has permitted us to understand this design, and view it as related to others which might otherwise have seemed curiosities.

When teachers who have used both the array (T_n) and the rods notice that there are bases whose halves are also integers, they can understand that many of the above results which were obtained in the common system are valid in other systems, if one merely replaces $\frac{1}{2} \times 10$ by the appropriate numeral, and uses the table of products in that base in a similar fashion. For example in base (IV), 32^2 and 31×33; 22^2 and 21×23; 12^2 and 11×13 follow the same rule as for 35^2 in the decimal system. If we know that $2 \times 1 — 2$, $2 \times 3 \sim 12$ and $3 \times 10 \sim 30$, we then have $12^2 \sim 210$, $11 \times 13 \sim 203$, $22^2 \sim 1210$, $21 \times 23 \sim 1203$, $32^2 \sim 3010$, $31 \times 33 \sim 3003$.

A teacher who wants to become a quick calculator now has access to a sound strategy. The first task is to return to the examples in Parts I and II of this book and use them to evolve a number of personal “milestones”. These milestones, extended over the various fields of mathematics, will supply an important loose network of relationships. Then practice, with or without paper and pencil, will make it clear how little has to be remembered; one will see that to be a quick and reliable calculator is a matter of algebra, not memory.

5 As a teacher pursues the mathematician in himself, he will notice that he, like a good mathematician, has need of safeguards which warn him when he has gone astray. Teachers can acquire these if they will learn to ask the questions which bring one’s attention to the crux and lead to the possession of criteria. Functioning criteria work by themselves and warn the learner that he has made an error. An error is not a thing to be ashamed of. On the contrary, it is a signal which says that mastery has not been achieved and the learner needs to do more work.

The following are the sort of questions that will lead to the formation of criteria:

1. How can you say “this” if you know “that” about the situation when “this” and “that” are contradictory?

2. Is it necessary to use so much energy in carrying out this operation?

3. If you look more closely at this problem, doesn’t it suggest its own solution?

These questions force awareness of what is particularly noticeable about a situation and nurture the scrutiny of a problem so as to unlock its unique solution.

Counter-examples are the most powerful means of disproving statements, and therefore the most useful to teachers. When one finds counter-examples easily, one knows that one’s criteria are functioning well and no elaborate dis-proof is required.

When teachers, instead of marking answers right or wrong, can throw students back to the situation to find criteria through the questions put to them, they will know that they have been educated as mathematicians and can in their turn provide mathematical education for their students. *There will be no need for anything else* because criteria are the guides to truth and because one must own them to be able to reach truth. It is they that will serve students, and only they.

6 Just as one can become aware of the dynamics of the mind, one can become aware of one's imagery and its dynamic. To be good at mathematics involves a command of one's imagery as it relates to the form of certain relationships. In a question involving say, the form $25n$, it is an image which links $25n$ to $\frac{1}{4} \times 100\text{n}$ or to $\frac{100n}{4}$ or to $100 \times \frac{n}{4}$. The dynamic of imagery is at work in the process which replaces the given form successively by other forms. By establishing a number of forms as triggers, one has access to a number of patterns which help make calculation faster.

To be able to use some of these visual relationships is a help to memory, and in turn memory helps by finding shortcuts for working out some problems and economizing in the use of operations.

Since the result of the cultivation of our imagery and its dynamic is that we are more sensitive to the nature of mental activities, it will be worth our while to work precisely on what matters for such ends. Good learning and good teaching will be the result, and teaching and learning, having come closer together, will support one another.

In these examples there has been no suggestion that teachers who want to educate themselves in order to make mathematicians of their students should study mathematics books and assimilate chapter upon chapter. On the contrary, the job of becoming more of a mathematician, as it has been described here, requires these awarenesses:

1 The cardinal notions of numeration, complementarity, and reading equations in various ways, yield addition and subtraction in all systems of numeration. Repeated subtraction yields long division.

2 The transformation of repeated additions into the autonomous operation of multiplication will yield products and fractions, powers and roots, logarithms, and an entry into the properties of numbers.

3 Quick calculations result from a vision of the set of equivalent expressions available for the patterns perceived, and the transformation of the given into those elements that again generate transformations which simplify and compress.

4 The more routes that can be found for going from one place to another, the better is the challenge understood.

5 To prove that I am independent is to follow any one of my inspirations, reject those which do not work, retain those which work and learn from both.

6 To see an answer as right (or wrong) is only a moment of feedback in the process of disentangling and no answer can be considered more important than the awareness of the problem and its demands upon my mind.

7 I can function as a knowing system on a multitude of levels: perceiving data, using language,

recognizing equivalences, and shift from one viewpoint to another, since all the elements can co-exist in my mind and I can order them at will as I do when I mobilize the equipment behind my speech, or play tennis, checkers or bridge, or cross a road with heavy traffic and no pedestrian crossings.

9 Teaching Mathematics to Children

In this chapter and the next we shall come as close as our understanding permits to offering a curriculum for teaching children in schools.

Of course it is clear that the teachers in their classrooms are the ones who face students and that they alone can decide what to do at each moment. The following is offered as a possible course open to every teacher who knows that no one can actually offer a course which works in all circumstances. Only within these terms of reference does it make sense for us to engage in the exercise that follows.

To work within our understanding of what it is to teach mathematics, let us keep in mind the following:

1. The hierarchy in the presentation of mathematical notions in this book has been that we move from

what can be perceived to what this can become when submitted to the mental transformations of which almost all children are capable.

2 Let us insist upon the fact that understanding has many meanings and that we can move ahead in a dialogue with youngsters when they understand what we are doing on one level even if they do not understand all that older or more experienced people could associate with the same situation.

For instance, it is possible to understand that in the sequence of names of numerals *thousand* comes after *hundred* without understanding that one thousand is equivalent to ten hundreds. It is possible to understand that two pears and three pears when put together end up as five pears and see that the same mental correspondence applies to two millions and three millions becoming five millions when put together, because the word millions replaces pears, and have no idea what one million describes as a count of, say, people or ants or grains of sugar.

3 A functioning child has noticed that pronouns can be used by everybody and that "I" can mean different people depending on who is speaking. He may know that "my mother" does or does not refer to the same person when used by his brothers and sisters and by other people, and therefore be prepared to recognize that there are stable elements in some situations as well as variable ones. This preparation will serve him well when he enters the field of mathematics.

At one level, *two plus three* (or 2 + 3 in signs) will generate the sound *five* (or sign 5) while leaving open the nature of the object to which these adjectives refer. What is stable is the dynamic correspondence $2 + 3 \rightarrow 5$ and what is variable is the so-called "concrete" material they apply to. So we shall not assume that children only understand when they are dealing with objects or with social elements such as money or shopping.

4 Because children can make sounds — as they prove by learning to speak — we shall not consider that making noises, like *complement* or *billion,* is a task beyond them.

Keeping in mind the fact that children who can see and hear do not confuse messages through the eyes with messages through the ears and are capable of coordinating these, it is easy to begin our work by bringing them to a state where they utter a sound for a sign, or point at a sign (until they learn how to write it) when hearing the corresponding sound.

By moving systematically from the correspondence

	1 (one)
to	1 (one) 2 (two)
to	1 (one) 2 (two) 3 (three) . . .
up to	1 (one) 2 (two) 3 (three) . . . . .9 (nine)

(the element in the brackets is the sound which is given *only once by* the teacher but practiced by the students as many times as he points to the sign) we can ensure assimilation of a game in which understanding means: *utter a sound for this sign* and *show me a sign for this sound.*

Teachers will do well to ensure that their presentation of these signs or sounds utilizes some of the numerous permutations of these signs. (There are 362,880 different ways of pointing once at each of the 9 signs, 1, 2, 3, . . . 9.) The "increasing" sequence 1, 2, 3 . . . 9 or the "decreasing" sequence 9, 8, 7 . . . 1 are only two of these and, although more common in counting up or down, they have the disadvantage of stifling the mind of young children who then associate numerals only with sequences and not with the answer to "how many?"

Let us note that in the array (T_n) we placed the units 1 through 9 on the top line because *ten* in mathematics means a unit of a higher order (only in one system is it also the name of the set of fingers.) The above exercise is one of sounds and signs, easily comprehended and fully mastered at that level.

There will be nothing to remember specially in this game and the test will remain within the terms of the game. If children of 5 or less can do it, they have proved that this sort of exercise is at their level. That they cannot do something else that has not yet been presented is entirely reasonable.

When we put together the game of the fingers and the game of naming or writing numerals, we obtain a new development permitting shifts of power from one field into another. This is the foundation of the curriculum-making presented here.

We associate the noise *one,* the sign 1, and any one of the fingers. We can show a finger and say, "Do you see *one* finger?" "And now?", changing the finger and repeating this change from any one finger to any other. Then we ask, “Show me *any one* of your fingers,” “Now another by itself, and another and another,” “Look at what your neighbor is doing. Is he showing *one* finger” “Is he showing the same finger as you are?” “Is it still true that he is showing one finger like you?”

“Show in turn one finger at a time starting with one thumb and ending with the other thumb.”

If some children can do it at once, use them to show others that the instructions can be understood, and that other children of their age can command their muscles to show any one finger in isolation. Give time to those who find it difficult.

In this or a subsequent lesson, ask for pairs of fingers to be formed on one hand or from fingers of both hands. *Do not* attempt to study how many pairs can be formed but use the variety (allowed by the 45 different possible pairs) to let children know that “a pair” is another name for *one and one,* that “two fingers” is the name for any pair, and that *two* is the representation used for any such pair, or any pair of anything besides fingers.

Subsequent lessons will be concerned with naming complements. A little practice will let the children know that if they show three fingers they do not show the complement in ten, and that they can find what it is by folding those three fingers and unfolding the others and counting them. Further, folding one more finger will produce an arrangement of six unfolded fingers. Folding those six and unfolding the others they find there are four, so

6 + 4, and also 1 + 9 or 2 + 8 or 3 + 7 or 5 + 5, describe unique arrangements of fingers.

Because we work on the set of fingers and do not use our fingers to represent “abstract” number, we cannot escape the formation of “clusters of relationships.” So, as they study a pair of complements in 10, beginners can investigate the complements within the complements, and in this way they will have many more chances to be intimately acquainted with each pair, and not to confuse them with each other.

These games will take as many lessons as children require to master the instructions, and as the interest they find in playing them permits. Do *not* attempt to get all children in your class involved at the same time. Rather work with those who find this kind of involvement easy and exciting. When some are on the way to independence you can either use them to involve other children or give them some written work to practice the notation.

1 *Simple transcription of perceptions:*

$9 + 1 \sim$ $\quad 7 + 3 \sim$ $\quad 4 + 6 \sim$

$2 + 8 \sim$ $\quad 6 + 4 \sim$ $\quad 5 + 5 \sim$

$3 + 7 \sim$ $\quad 1 + 9 \sim$ $\quad 8 + 2 \sim$

2 *Which name is missing?*

$\quad + 1 \sim 10$ $\quad \quad + 7 \sim 10$ $\quad \quad 8 + \quad \sim 10$ etc.

3 *Which pairs make ten?*

in words: teacher or advanced student listens

in figures: use the notation (,) for a pair; the order of writing the figures can produce different ways of writing the same pair

4 *Fill in the gap* (only pairs of complements in 10 are required)

(1,); (,3); (4,); (,6); (,9); (9,); etc.

The notation for subtraction is another possible exercise at this level. Teachers can present a succession of notations which yield the same answer but through different procedures.

+ 3 ~ 10 (,3) (3,)

The teacher can say, "If from ten (showing both hands open) I *take away* 3, what am i left with?" The answer, if forthcoming, can then be written as 10 — 3 and read as "ten take away three" or "ten *minus* 3." Neither form is preferable nor requires special care at this level. What has been done is to provide a language and a notation for subtraction as another way of reading addition and complements.

To test assimilation it will be sufficient to propose problems of the following kind.

With two hands: (10 — 3) + 2 + 1 ~
With one hand: (5 — 2) + 1 ~

giving the questions first in words and then in writing.

What we must watch at this level is that children recognize that the notation triggers speech which involves instructions that can be carried out on one's fingers. The answer is the last thing one says — the label for the set at rest after the operations have been completed.

There may be some children for whom the fascination of their fingers or the games on the array is limited. For these people and the others the *Algebricks* may serve as an entry into mathematics compatible with their interest in building with a flexible and colorful material.

Since the rods are prisms, when they are used in play to make buildings they become involved in a vast number of relationships which have spatial meaning. There is potential for algebraic and numerical meanings in these relationships as well. It is the teacher's responsibility to observe the spontaneous building of each child and note which properties of the rods he is exploring through his staircases, towers, cubes, trains, etc., to extend these activities, and introduce some games which will give the learner an entry into seeing some relationships he may not yet have found on his own.

The following are some of the most primitive observations that can be made about the rods:

1 The set of rods subdivides into subsets whose elements are rods of one color; the rods of each such class are now defined by their distinctive colors.

2 Rods of one color are also equivalent because of their dimensions; any one rod of any one color can replace any other of the same color in any pattern made of rods.

3 Rods of different colors are unequal; there is one class of the largest and one of the smallest rods, and when these are removed there may still be two classes left, one of the smallest and one of the largest, and so on, until there are two classes left containing the yellow rods and the dark green rods.

4 If one rod of each color is selected, they can be placed side by side to produce a staircase.

5 Two such staircases can be interlocked to form rectangles. In two of the ways this can be done the rods of one staircase are end-to-end with the rods in the other; in one case the white is end-to-end with orange but in the other it is end-to-end with blue.

6 This interlocking is equivalent to saying that the difference between two successive rods is equal to a white rod.

7 This last statement makes the white rod the only rod which can measure exactly all the others.

8 By making these measurements rods can be called equivalent to trains of white rods and labeled by counting the number of rods in the trains.

9 Hence it is possible to shift from the perception that, say, a brown rod is larger than a black one, to the statement that 8 is bigger than 7, provided one

keeps in mind that these numerals refer to trains of white rods.

10 Starting with such trains and scattering the coaches, while keeping them perceptibly close together, one can extend the meaning of *larger* or *smaller* to sets and from there to the comparison of the numerals, in this way giving meaning to "eight is bigger than seven." (Until now we could only say that in the sequence of noises from one to nine, *eight* came after *seven* and seven before *eight. Before* and *after* has an immediate meaning in the experience of the sequence of sounds, and *bigger* and *larger* in the case of rods. Now a bridge has been established between these very different kinds of experiences.)

11 Rods can be placed to produce trains and the length of such trains is perceptible and can serve to produce a feeling of a magnitude capable of being made larger by addition of other rods, or smaller by the suppression of some at its ends.

12 Challenges emerge through the naming of relationships:

- Giving a name to the smaller rod in a pair after finding that a rod can be measured exactly with another one. This creates the fractional terminology which, except for *one half,* uses the ordinal adjectives for its expression.

- Finding that many names describe any given rod according to whether addition, subtraction, multiplication or fraction is the relevant perceptual pointer:

$$p \sim 2 \times r \sim g + w \sim y - w \sim \frac{1}{2} \times t \sim \frac{2}{5} \times o.$$

- Finding that it is normal for every object to have an infinite number of names and for every name to apply to an infinite number of objects.

13 Inequality is *transitive;* i.e. from two statements arising from perception, such as $y < b$ and $b < t$, we can ensure that $y < t$, not from perception, but by implication confirmed by perception.

14 Three rods can be related by, say, $p < y < b$, providing a chain of relationships with a middle term, while unless we do something to recast our reading, $y > p$ and $y < b$ tell us two distinct things about rods in pairs.

15 It is possible to articulate perception through mental dynamics, to read in a staircase a multitude of relationships and to attempt to bring them together, as, for example:

$w < r < g < p < y < d < b < t < B < o$

or

$w < r, w < g, w < p, w < y, w < d, w < b, w < t, w < B, w < o$

or

$w < r, r < g, g < p, p < y, y < d, d < b, b < t, t < B, B < o.$

16 It is possible to use sight to find a length equal to any one of the trains made of a small number of rods, particularly the smaller ones.

17 Estimation of the difference between two lengths can become second nature and can lead to classes of equivalence such as

$w \sim r - w \sim g - r \sim p - g \sim y - p \ldots \sim o - B$
$r \sim g - w \sim p - r - y - g \sim \ldots\ldots \sim o - t$ and so on.

18 A family of rectangles may be constructed by placing rods of one color side by side, and each member of this family may be exactly covered by placing rods of one color side by side across the length of it.

19 Occasionally one of the covering rectangles will be the same color as the rectangle beneath it. We call this special case in the family of rectangles a *square* and make other squares, depending on which color rod we use to generate the family.

20 Building upward in equal layers from the foundation of a square a point is reached where the height of the building is measurable by the rod which measures the length and width of its base. We can call this special building a *cube* and construct other cubes of the same dimensions using different colored rods. Some rods can be used for this purpose and some cannot.

21 If we stand a rod on end and think of it as a post or pillar, it has certain dimensions; pillars of the same dimensions can be built using other rods so as to support a beam. If we build pillars with white rods or rods of one color they look alike, but if we use rods of different colors there are many arrangements and the same collection of rods can be used to make different pillars. The pillar can be

seen to have a volume in terms of the number of white cubes it takes to build it, or the number of red prisms, etc.

Obviously there are many more lessons to be learned at the primitive level of perception and action. These are therefore appropriate for teaching beginners of any age and will serve all students well, particularly very young ones.

We have restricted ourselves in this chapter so far to the top line of the array (T_n) and the rods in the box of *Algebricks*. Nothing in what we have done forces us to hold to the language these have put into circulation. Clearly what we did in Parts I and II can be taken up again here. We can re-name a finger or the white rod with the label ty or *hundred* and generate corresponding names for any subset of fingers or any rod, and in this way carry over all the perceptions already gathered into new-sounding statements and new writings.

Let us not forget that in our presentation of numeration we can easily introduce different bases by placing a vertical line in the array and prohibiting the use of the signs on the right of that line. Beginners can understand this game and quickly learn to count in any base.

We have treated this matter in other chapters and recommend it to teachers of beginners mainly because it means presenting the truth on this subject to anyone. From such an introduction students will gain a proper understanding of numerals as a system of labeling and will avoid being confused at a later date.

In the field of computation the decimal system is not preferable to others in spite of its established dominance.

10 Generating a Mathematics Curriculum

Since the previous chapters have made readers acquainted with the principles, the ideas, the techniques and materials that can make anyone into a mathematician, at least in the fields of algebra and arithmetic, there may be need to examine how a curriculum can be produced.

The approach we have studied takes many liberties with both traditional and "new math" sequences and it may leave readers wondering what curriculum, or sequence of mathematical topics, to follow.

The chart in Appendix B shows one map of the territory of elementary mathematics that I made several years ago but which can still serve to show that there is not one curriculum but a multiplicity of possible curricula. The diagram will make it clear how many paths can be constructed, each of which could reach all the topics listed there. The diagram may not give up all its secrets at once, but I urge readers to take time to study it.

My mathematics textbooks show only one of the possibilities, but the one chosen is worked out in great detail — enough, in fact, for them to be suitable for independent use by students. My workshops over the years and the texts written by some of the people who have worked with me since 1954 offer other alternatives.

In order to give teachers some insight into my texts and the spirit in which they were written, and bring about in them awarenesses which propel them towards independence, I have chosen here to list some of the principal characteristics of Books 1 through 7, and to discuss in some detail one of the texts (Book 4, Fractions) which concerns an area of mathematics ordinarily considered "difficult" by teachers.

The Characteristics of Gattegno Mathematics, Books 1—7

1. Books 1—7 are "open books," which means that they seek to present questions in such a way that they are accompanied by the tools for answering them, and therefore are not dependent on a linear development and can be entered at any point.
2. The tools which are given are based on an awareness of the dynamics of the mind, especially as it has been demonstrated in the mastery of

speech by almost all students before they go to school.

3 Therefore the sequence followed is one that moves from the level of perception and action to that of verbalization and notation. (This is the movement we followed in the first seven chapters of this book.)

4 There is no need to think of any student as lacking anything which these books will provide. In as much as the questions they present are at the level of perception, anyone with sense organs and a functioning mind is already equipped to find his way towards mastery of the skills involved. Each person will involve himself at the level he finds himself, needing or not needing to practice what is presented, and deciding for himself which is the case. The books aim to offer enough experience to satisfy people who need many exercises and enough variety to challenge the most adventurous.

5 In all cases the books leave to the learner the judgment of Tightness and correctness, and they give him access to criteria which allow that he will have the awareness necessary to know if he is proceeding accurately.

6 Rather than give the learner the feeling that he has exhausted the subject matter, the books seek to whet his appetite for further study.

Fractions

Book 4 includes one chapter presenting fractions as operators; one as families of ordered pairs and the operations on them; one on decimals as a new language, and a small section on percentages as a question of notation.

Fractions as Operators

Because fractions are defined as the inverses of multiples we have met them as soon as we have met multiplication and its language. To each multiple corresponds a fraction. The fractional language itself allows us to perceive that we can ask for one object linked to another if we at the same time name the relationship. For example to ask for one half of a given rod is to ask for an object, a rod in this case. Hence "one half" seems to tell someone to do something and this awareness is associated with the word *operator*.

As soon as fractional operators gain a reality of their own they can be studied *per se* and we soon find that a special dynamics called the *"fractional calculus"* will provide awareness of the universe of operators. For example, it is possible to operate on operators and find an operator which is equivalent to an operator upon another operator. *One half of,* or $\frac{1}{2}\times$, can be *iterated* and produces operators such as $\frac{1}{2} \times \frac{1}{2} \times \ldots . \frac{1}{2} \times$ any number of times.*

Each operator forms a class of equivalence based on its relation to its inverse operator. *Twice one half* of, $2 \times \frac{1}{2} \times$, is equivalent to $1 \times$ (or once) — that is, the *"identity operator."* There are any number of such expressions: $\frac{1}{2} \times 2 \times \sim \frac{1}{2} \times \frac{1}{2} \times 2 \times 2 \times \sim 2 \times \frac{1}{2} \times \frac{1}{2} \times 2 \times \sim \ldots$ The identity operator has an infinity of expressions each belonging to an infinite class, for where we wrote $\frac{1}{2}$ we can write $\frac{1}{3} \times$, or $\frac{1}{4} \times$ etc. and where we wrote $2 \times$, we could have written $3 \times$, or $4 \times \ldots$ etc.

Likewise for any operator.

The shortest name of an operator can be singled out or not. To know what is the function of its shortest name is more important than knowing how to obtain it as an "answer."

The algebra of operators can be introduced in a number of ways. What is vital in approaching the subject is that the teacher recognizes that the awareness governing operators rests on the

---

* In elementary schools it is customary to restrict this study to finding the operator equivalent to, say, $\frac{1}{2} \times \frac{1}{3} \times$, and even then one of these is not treated as an operator but as an object: $\frac{1}{2} \times \left(\frac{1}{3}\right)$ or one half of (one third.)

perception that one object may be linked to another by a relationship, the essential difference between perceiving one object and perceiving two.

Ordered Pairs

Given a pair of rods, they are linked by a relationship we call a fraction. Because there are two rods, in general we do not get only one relationship between them, but two, according to which we use as a measure and which as the one being measured. Hence all rods which are measurable with another rod provide a pair (x,y) in which x is the measured and y the measure. Whole numbers or integers are therefore ordered pairs in which the second term is called the unit. Where we are used to writing 2, 3, 4, etc., we can now write (2,1), (3,1), (4,1), etc.

This brief exposition contains all that is required to establish an important shift of viewpoint. Let the reader be sure he is alert to the significance of the following aspects.

1. We start by focusing on a relationship between two rods and then detach it from them until it becomes an entity which we can study *per se*.

2. Although any pair of rods will suggest two such relationships, when we write, say, (t,y) we arbitrarily decide to mean the relationship of the tan rod measured by the yellow rod. Given this decision, (y,t) refers to a different relationship. The order of the elements in a *written* pair is therefore significant.

3 Since (t,w) has been given the meaning of the relationship obtained when the tan rod is measured by the white rod, which is the process we earlier used to associate a numeral (8) to the tan rod, we see that we can regard all the integers as special cases included in the class of relationships we are now considering.

4 Since the pair (t,y) can also be written (8,5) by changing the names given to the rods into numerals, we see that a fraction can be represented as an ordered pair of numerals.

Indeed, if we replace the notation (8,5) by the notation $\frac{8}{5}$, we produce the familiar written form of a fraction.

Classes of Equivalence and Operations

There are two distinct ways of generating classes of equivalence for any given fraction. I have called these *Equivalence-A* and *Equivalence-M* to remind us that the first allows us to add fractions and the other allows us to multiply them.

Equivalence-A

This equivalence is based on the perception that if we start with any pair (a,b) we can obtain equivalent pairs (of trains) by taking the same number of a as of b.

That is, $(a,b) \sim (a + a, b + b) \sim (a + a + a, b + b + b) \sim$

$$(2 \times a, 2 \times b) \sim (3 \times a, 3 \times b) \sim \dots$$

$(n \times a, n \times b)$ where n is any integer.

In effect, this says that the relationship between a and b is preserved if we take the same multiples of the object to be measured and the object that measures it.

Clearly we can look at this process the other way round and say that we can find equivalent pairs by dividing the elements instead of multiplying them. If a and b have any common divisors then we can get more pairs equivalent to (a,b) by dividing both a and b by them. When we divide a and b by their biggest common divisor (i.e. their HCF) we must obtain a pair, (p,q) say, in which the elements have no common divisor (excluding 1.) (p,q) is said to be an

irreducible pair (and the fraction $\frac{p}{q}$ is *in lowest terms.)*

We can now see that to generate a *complete* class of equivalent pairs we must begin with an irreducible pair and systematically take all the multiples of its elements by the sequence of numerals.

Addition

Before we can decide how to develop a procedure for adding fractions we need to know what meanings we can give to such an operation, and we will look for clues in what we already know, both about fractions and about addition. We know from our work with fractional operators on lengths that if we have, say, $\frac{2}{7}$

of a length and add it to $\frac{3}{7}$ of the same length we will have altogether $\frac{5}{7}$ of it — and that this statement is independent of the particular length we worked on. It seems natural to shift attention, and therefore language and notation, from the idea of adding the lengths to the idea of adding the operators and writing, simply, $\frac{3}{7} + \frac{2}{7} \sim \frac{5}{7}$.

Speech allows us to absorb this kind of statement into the pattern of many others that we often use:

> 3 cows and 2 cows are 5 cows altogether
> 3 hundred plus 2 hundred is equivalent to 5 hundred
> 3 sevenths plus 2 sevenths is equivalent to 5 sevenths.

This suggests that we can give a mathematical definition in the following way. Given two fractions $\frac{x}{y}$ and $\frac{t}{u}$, we will say that $\frac{a}{b}$ is their sum, and will write $\frac{x}{y}+\frac{t}{u}\sim\frac{a}{b}$ if $\frac{a}{b}$ of M (where M is any magnitude whatever) gives the same result as $\frac{x}{y}$ of M added to $\frac{t}{u}$ of M.

We can put this definition into operation immediately on any example where y and *u* are the same number — that is, where the two given fractions have the same denominator — because, as we saw with the example of the sevenths, it reduces to the already familiar addition of integers. So, for example.

$$\frac{1}{7}+\frac{5}{7}\sim\frac{6}{7};\ \frac{8}{11}+\frac{9}{11}\sim\frac{17}{11};\ \frac{91}{123}+\frac{18}{123}+\frac{109}{123}$$

For all other cases, when y and u are not the same number, we can use *equivalence-A* to transform the problem into one which can be solved by the same simple procedure.

$\frac{x}{y}$ is one member of an infinite equivalence class of fractions.

Another member of this class must be one which has the denominator $u \times y$; in fact, it is the fraction $\frac{u \times x}{u \times y}$.

Similarly one of the fractions equivalent to $\frac{t}{u}$ is $\frac{y \times t}{y \times u}$.

Therefore we can transform the problem of finding $\frac{y \times t}{y \times u}$ into the problem of finding $\frac{u \times x}{u \times y} + \frac{y \times t}{y \times u}$.

But since $u \times y$ is equivalent to $y \times u$, the denominators of the two fractions are now the same number and the question is in the simple form that we can immediately solve.

Following this procedure in a particular case, let us solve the question $\frac{3}{7} \sim \frac{8}{9}$. We start by finding an equivalent to $\frac{3}{7}$ with denominator 9×7, and to $\frac{8}{9}$ with denominator 7×9.

$$\text{Thus } \frac{3}{7}+\frac{8}{9} \text{ transforms to } \frac{9\times3}{9\times7}+\frac{7\times8}{7\times9}$$

$$\sim\frac{27}{63}+\frac{56}{63}$$

$$\sim\frac{83}{63}$$

The details of whether this answer can now be transformed into a mixed number, or whether it can be reduced, do not bring any new matters of importance. The main point is that we have shown how *equivalence-A* can give us access to the familiar rules about "common denominators" and dispel the mysteries of the addition procedure.

Multiplication and Equivalence-M

Our first acquaintance with another way of combining two fractions to get a third may be when we notice that we can make sense of questions like:

> "What is one half of one half of the tan rod?"
>
> "What is two-thirds of three-fifths of the orange rod?"
>
> "What is seven-fifths of five-fourths of the pink rod?"

In these cases we are again operating on lengths, but instead of operating twice on the same length (as when we spoke of adding,) we are operating first on one length and then on the result of the first operation. Taking the third question, for instance, we know that we can find $\frac{5}{7}$ of the pink rod, which is the yellow rod, and then find $\frac{7}{5}$ of the yellow rod — that is, the black rod.

But we can also notice that the same end result could be obtained by a single fractional operation — "What is seven-fourths of the pink rod?" So $\frac{7}{5}$ *of* $\frac{5}{7}$ *of the pink rod* is equivalent to $\frac{7}{5}$ *of the pink rod.* Since it is evident that the equivalence is not dependent on the length operated on we can shift attention to the relation between the operators and write, simply, $\frac{7}{5} \sim \frac{5}{4} \sim \frac{7}{4}$.

This suggests that we can define the multiplication of fractions as producing the single fraction that is equivalent to "a fraction of a fraction." Given two fractions $\frac{x}{y}$ and $\frac{t}{u}$ we will say that $\frac{c}{d}$ is their product, and write $\frac{x}{t} \times \frac{t}{u} \sim \frac{c}{d}$, if $\frac{c}{d}$ of *M* (where *M* is any magnitude whatever) gives the same result as $\frac{x}{y}$ of

$[\frac{7}{1} \times \frac{1}{4} \sim \frac{7}{2} \times \frac{2}{4} \sim \frac{7}{3} \times \frac{3}{4} \sim$ of M].

We can now deal with the task of computing products by introducing the idea of *equivalence-M.*

We have already observed that $\frac{7}{5} \sim \frac{5}{4} \sim \frac{7}{4}$ and we can readily see that we could just as well have obtained, say,

$$\frac{7}{3} \times \frac{3}{4} \sim \frac{7}{4}$$

or $\frac{7}{8} \times \frac{8}{4} \sim \frac{7}{4}$

or, indeed, $\frac{7}{n} \times \frac{n}{4} \sim \frac{7}{4}$, where *n* is any integer. In short, we have an equivalence class of products: $\frac{7}{1} \times \frac{1}{4} \sim \frac{7}{2} \times \frac{2}{4} \sim \frac{7}{3} \times \frac{3}{4} \sim \ldots$

This generation of an equivalence class can be generalized through the perception that if $\frac{H}{K}$ is an irreducible pair we can use any number C as an intermediary and measure *H* by C and C by *K*.

Then $\frac{H}{C} \times \frac{C}{K}$ will be equivalent to $\frac{H}{K}$ for all values of C.

So we can immediately write down the fraction which is equivalent to $\frac{x}{y} \times \frac{t}{u}$ in all cases where *y* and *t* are the same number. When they are not, *equivalence-A* tells us that one of the pairs in the family $\frac{x}{y}$ will be $\frac{t \times x}{t \times y}$ and one in the family $\frac{t}{u}$ will be $\frac{y \times t}{y \times u}$. These are the pairs that will allow us to contract $\frac{t \times x}{t \times y} \times \frac{t \times x}{u \times y}$ into $\frac{t \times x}{u \times y}$ by means of *equivalence-M*.

Therefore if $\frac{c}{d}$ is the product of $\frac{x}{y} \times \frac{t}{u}$, $c \sim x \times t$ and $d \sim y \times u$.

This can be recognized as the conventional method of multiplying fractions by taking the product of their numerators and putting it above the product of their denominators.

Equivalence-M will also allow us to perform division of fractions. We will read $\frac{a}{b} \div \frac{c}{d} \sim \frac{x}{y}$ as the inverse of a multiplication in which $\frac{c}{d} \times \frac{x}{y} \sim \frac{a}{b}$. By *equivalence-M* we know that if *c* and *a* are the same number, then we can contract immediately. Therefore, by using *equivalence-A,* if we find pairs equivalent to $\frac{c}{d}$ and $\frac{a}{b}$ such that the numerators are the same, $(c \times a)$ we have $\frac{c \times a}{d \times a} \times \frac{x}{y} \sim \frac{c \times a}{c \times b}$ and thus $x \sim d \times a$ and $y \sim c \times b$.

The quotient $\frac{x}{y}$ is found to be obtainable by taking the *cross product* of the numerators and denominators: $\frac{a}{b} \div \frac{c}{d} \sim \frac{a \times d}{b \times c}$.
This is the rule everyone learned in school, but here it appears only as an attribute of operations with fractions based on *equivalence-M* and *equivalence-A.*

Decimals

The section on decimals in Book 4 is treated as a job of translation. First the notation of the decimal point is given as an alternative to placing a number of zeros in the denominator of a fraction chosen to be decimal (in that its denominator is a power of ten or can be expressed as such.)

We write $\frac{1}{10} \sim 0.1$, $\frac{1}{100} \sim 0.01$, $\frac{1}{1000} \sim 0.001$, and so on. The appearance of the answer in operations with these fractions is easily transferred and can serve as the basis for calculation with decimal fractions in either form.

Thus, $\frac{1}{10}$ becomes $0.1 + 0.3 \sim 0.4$, and conversely.

$\frac{23}{100} + \frac{15}{100} \sim \frac{38}{100}$ becomes $0.23 + 0.15 \sim 0.38$, and conversely, etc.

Indeed when we treat decimals as a new language we make sense at once of the new notation, which in the beginning only describes what is already known and only later becomes a tool that permits us to ask new kinds of questions which make sense in the new context. For instance as soon as one becomes aware that sometimes there are a finite number of digits on the right side of the decimal point ($\frac{1}{5}$— 0.2) and sometimes an infinite number ($\frac{1}{3} \sim 0.3333\ldots$) the question of making them uniform arises. It can be solved by making all decimal fractions have an infinite number of digits, noting that if, for example, $\frac{1}{5}$ is written as 0.1999 . . . the difference between 0.2 and 0.1999 . . . must be written 0.0000 . . .

But as soon as this becomes part of one's knowledge and the perception of a decimal calls up its class of equivalence, as happens with fractions, new questions emerge. One interesting question with far-reaching consequences concerns the structure of the infinite sequence of digits. There are only a few possible alternatives to consider:

1 All the digits could be the same. Are there many such examples?

2 The infinite number of digits could be made of an infinite repetition of the same group of digits. Are there many such examples?

3 The phenomenon (b) could appear after an initial portion of the sequence which is not repeated.

4 Are there other kinds of regularities one can think of? Do these two cases (c) and (d) concern a small or large portion of the class of decimals?

5 What about irregularities? Do they occur? How frequently? Do they lead to a new awareness of the relationship between numbers and decimal forms? For instance if we start by calling a number any infinite sequence of digits as met here, what kinds of numbers can we generate from this? Do we recuperate those already met?

Because this thinking only requires common sense it is available to everyone and the mere asking of these questions may lead us to become curious about the answers. This is the inner climate of the mathematician. We can now let everyone have a chance to understand the questions and decide for himself whether he wishes to give himself or not to a study of them.

Naturally even when simply expressed, these questions can be profound and demanding.

Here we have discussed the requirements of the teaching of decimals from the point of view of making it accessible to perception. Every time we can take a question from any field and make it a question of perception — in the sense we use it when we handle language — we allow years of intimate experience to become available, however young the student is. This we have been able to do in the example above.

Percentages

Percentages are presented in Book 4 as the name of the numerator when the denominator of a fraction is 100. Nothing more needs to be known or said.

Summing Up

When I wanted to bring awareness of the relationships involved in fractions to readers of Book 4, I allowed the relationships themselves to suggest to me a vocabulary for dealing with them. Thus to see fractions as the inverses of multiples and call them operators made a good deal more sense than to give them the definition their etymology suggests ("breaking into bits").

In considering ordered pairs, the powers of transformation which allow a person to use the correct pronoun in his native language allow the generation of families of equivalent expressions. *He, him, me* and *I* may all refer to the same person, depending on the point of view, the speaker and the function in the sentence. In the same way "one half" applies to an infinity of different pairs, thus unifying them (1 is $\frac{1}{2} \times 2$; 2 is $\frac{1}{2} \times 4$; 3 is $\frac{1}{2} \times 6$ . . .) At the same time *one half* can be distinguished as a sound from *two fourths, three sixths,* etc., which are equivalent expressions. It is easy here to see why equivalent expressions are such powerful pedagogical tools, unifying and separating at the same time.

In the case of operations with fractions, the families of equivalence generated through the two modes, *equivalence-M* and *equivalence-A,* provided all that was needed to allow the operations of addition, subtraction, multiplication and division to be extended from integers to fractions. Thus it was not necessary to present rules — "find common denominators," "invert and multiply," etc. — which apply exclusively to operations with fractions.

Similarly, by viewing decimal fractions as a new language, we were allowed to enter into the questions specifically generated by decimals and explore some areas which would have been inaccessible to us otherwise.

This section can perhaps serve readers as a paradigm of a way of constructing a curriculum that takes both the subject matter and the powers of the learner into account.

Postscript

What is it, then, that will allow us to teach mathematics to anyone with a functioning mind and an inclination to learn? Simply, finding a way to make the learner aware of the powers of his mind — the powers he uses everyday, those which allowed him to learn his native language and to use imagery and symbolism. This means that the job of teaching is one of bringing about self-awareness in learners through whatever means are available in the environment: words, actions, perceptions of transformations, one's fingers, one's language, one's memory, one's games, one's symbolisms, one's inner and outer wealth of perceived relationships, and so on.

Because technology, at the electronic level of today, has made it possible to reach millions instead of scores, in the future all valid educational ideas will end up available on television, reaching people through computers and satellites rather than through textbooks and teachers at schools.

This era is with us already and calling us to do the new job the best we can.

Appendix A: A Prelude to the Science of Education *

Since Aristotle men have wanted to make statements about the world which were both neutral and universal: neutral so that the speaker and the listener only felt involved in the content and not in their own idiosyncrasies, and universal so that no example could be imagined that contradicted the content of the statement, unless by doing so it led to a new discovery. Thus 'all objects fall' can be tested to be true by everyone, and if any objects don't it must be because their weight is balanced by an equal force.

.In this paper we shall discuss whether we can make statements about education, and in particular about the teaching of

---

* Reprinted from "Mathematics Teaching," the Bulletin of the Association of Teachers of Mathematics No. 59, Summer, 1972

mathematics, which are neutral and universal and do represent progress in our awareness of what we are considering.

Before doing this it may be useful to the reader to examine whether the usual statements made by educators, or about education by anyone else, are received as neutral, universal statements which can be treated as true or false, or simply as statements of opinion which are true or false depending only on the examples quoted in support. For example, if we say 'Children learn at their own pace' or 'Mathematics is difficult for many children' or 'The study of dead languages is boring,' are we actually saying any more than that rumor has it that it is not possible to make people learn at a single pace, or make mathematics attractive and easy, or the study of dead languages an exciting adventure?

Until now, I claim, educators have not been attracted to making a science of their activities; that is, they have preferred guidance from the views of their leaders to developing the criteria which would produce knowledge in their field comparable in certainty with that reached in the sciences.

This does not mean that it is not possible to find such criteria and to develop a science of education. Not to have tried is not equivalent to having shown its impossibility, and we shall prove here that it is possible simply by trying.

The usual demand made by the sciences of scientists is that they be *with* their problems and let these guide their steps. A scientist gives himself to the subject he studies and only wishes to make statements which are valid about it. The will to remain with the problem leads by itself to the avoidance of distractions and the emergence of those features which can be reported to present themselves when one contemplates the given subject.

In the field of education it is in no way different. But the complexity may be a challenge and the statements be complicated sometimes because men are unique in that their wills generate true differences which weigh more than their true similarities. By selecting ways of working and problems of a certain kind it remains possible to reach the same objectivity and usefulness found in other sciences. It may also be possible to attract more workers for this science than seem today to wish to concentrate on these problems.

This paper also aims to be an inducement to its readers to consider the fulfillment that is possible in becoming scientists for education. Since it appears in a periodical for teachers of mathematics the examples worked out will mainly be taken from the study of that field. Other teachers will add their own examples.

Let us first assume that some agreement exists on the following points. We all are 'learning systems,' that is, we know how to change the time that life gives us into experiences which are capable of being evoked, whilst time itself is consumed irretrievably. To learn is a property of the living or of the process by which we transform the given into what is, into what is ours from then on. But since other people learn and what is theirs could save us time if it were available for our own use as and when we want it, we are all prepared to learn from others. All of us value a reduction of our time of learning so long as this does not take away from us joy, enjoyment, the fulfillment of our duty, etc. We shall call that part of our education *the transformation of our self* which uses parts of this self to objectify what others have objectified for themselves.

It is unnecessary for us all to agree upon values — which differ from person to person — before we can find a treatment of some educational matters that is acceptable to everybody.

It is clear, for instance, that there is a difference between the change of our time into experience resulting from our mere functionings, such as looking or listening, and that resulting from our acceptance of what someone else has codified for his convenience. When looking, listening, thinking, etc., are involved on their own we need no one other than ourselves and nothing other than time to find ourselves having experiences which can be singled out, perhaps to be expressed in words or forms of our own. But we also use these same functionings on materials which are conventional, not 'necessary', as far as we are concerned, and which cannot be worked on until some part of our self has been given to becoming something *within* our self that can be acted upon.

There are, here, clearly, two very different processes involved: one concerning itself with objectivation, the reserving of mental energy in order to make the material into *objects* within the self on which the mental powers of the self can operate; the other concerning itself with these *operations,* the dynamics of the mind.

The mind of someone who has objectified part of his self may after a while no longer distinguish between these two processes, and not notice that the objectified energy — which has gained a structure — is less labile than the links between the objectified energies. This is the case with images, visual or auditory memory, the vocabulary of our languages, etc. Most of us have lost the power to discriminate between them and those of our functionings that act upon them.

When we are in the process of studying a second (or new) language we find that the retention of vocabulary differs from the use of words in spontaneous sentences. But once we have mastered a language, thought and verbalization seem to be one and the same thing.

To make these distinctions more prominent we shall use a special word for the mobilization of the energy within the objectified element. We shall call *ogden* a unit of learning which refers precisely to this mobilization. That is, every time we find ourselves in possession of a structured part of our mental energy caused by our response to a situation in which our self is involved, we shall say that we have paid one ogden in order to own the structuration of the energy rather than the unstructured energy that went into it. Ogdens are thus required to 'clip' or 'retain' any mental quantum which cannot be the result of one's own ordinary functionings alone. When we manage, for instance, to retain a word from our own or any other language we have paid an ogden for this. If we can use the word again and again we know that we paid the required ogden; if we cannot bring it back at once, either we did not truly pay the ogden or some mechanism prevents its recall.

Languages are made of vocabularies and other components. For each word in the vocabulary we have to pay an ogden whether we get it through translation or mere recall. Thus vocabularies are expensive in terms of ogdens. So are grammatical rules and conjugation paradigms. But there are less expensive means of obtaining the uses of languages once we know how to avoid asking for unnecessary ogdens — that is, when learners can reach through an awareness of their inner dynamics those elements that students of foreign languages are usually asked only to retain. This saving of ogdens only results when this study of how the dynamics of the mind (which is everyone's birthright) produces new knowledge out of pre-existing knowledge has been made. This we shall not do here but only say that it is the object of study of epistemology, the science of how we know.

Ogdens, being required for what cannot be invented by everybody, will find their place in the linguistic aspects of any form of learning, mathematics included, because they are the most economical way of owning what may otherwise take years to be found again. But, ogdens belonging to the life of the mind are only well spent when they make the self more competent in its attack on future tasks. Learning becomes part of growth only when the spent ogdens become part of the invested capital of energy, not when they are in the memory as isolated items.

For many a primary school child arithmetical facts have had to be bought with hundreds of ogdens, requiring innumerable further ogdens for the facts to be kept available, instead of his having the dynamic knowledge that results from the investment of the strictly minimal number of ogdens.

That today we can look at arithmetic teaching and learning with such detail and precision is a sign that the science of education is in the making. The following illustrations will serve to make the precision obvious to all readers.

1 Estimation of the ogdens required to learn the common system of numeration.

- *The spoken language of the English numerals.*

Every child finds in his environment the sounds of some numerals used as adjectives. He must pay nine ogdens for the numerals under ten; one for -teen and then four more for eleven, twelve, thirteen, fifteen, which are irregular, and none for nineteen, eighteen, seventeen, sixteen, and fourteen; one for -ty and then four more for ten, twenty, thirty, fifty, which are irregular, and none for ninety, eighty, seventy, sixty, and forty; one for one hundred; one for a thousand; one for a million, etc. Hence the accountancy for speaking numerals which he has heard is the free combinatoric upon material costing twenty-two ogdens.

The fact that the numerals are ordered is an additional structure upon the set of these sounds and perhaps one or more ogdens will be required for the establishment of the *sequence* between one and nine. These same ogdens can be used for the sequence after twenty; another amount will be required from ten to sixteen, usable when we go from sixteen to nineteen.

An ogden is required for the maintenance of hundred as the first sound to utter when three numerals are involved (a special case of attention to silence when the middle numeral is missing may also be worth an ogden.) Another ogden will suffice to leap over the stretch from one thousand to nine hundred ninety-nine thousand, nine hundred ninety-nine; and a single one more for one million to jump from this to the one preceding one billion (American.)

The balance sheet shows:

> *Capital investment:* twenty-four ogdens.
> *Returns:* one billion numerals.

Of course this is a very conservative estimate and this investment could have produced a lot more. For instance instead of a billion we could use 'thousand million', which will cost one ogden, but will be re-usable when million million is followed by thousand million million and so on.

In fact no one needs to make investments beyond the twenty-four mentioned because no one will ever wish to name such numerals *per se.*

- The written language is a different matter and some of man's activities may require the writing of particular numerals with a certain number of digits (thirty or so say.) Here the availability of the spoken numerals will reduce the investment, but possibly only very little. Indeed we must again pay ogdens to link firmly 1 with one, 2 with two, . . . 9 with nine, and pay again twenty ogdens for the reading and writing of numerals up to 999, one for the comma for one thousand and one for the comma of one million. One ogden has to be paid for the 0 which fills the empty place between the units of different orders, and one not to write the 0 on the left of a two figure number. One ogden has to be paid for the convention of writing horizontally and reading from the left. Hence the study of the common system of numeration in English requires exactly forty-eight ogdens to be mastered from scratch.

2 Estimation of the ogdens required to learn all systems of numeration which employ Arabic numerals.

- *Systems with a base smaller than that of the common system.*

The cost is NIL. Indeed in the array used in 1(b) it is sufficient to place one bar after the three elements of any one column and to restrict oneself to the elements on the left of that bar to obtain all numerals in that base exactly as it was obtained in the common system.*

- *Systems with a base larger than that of the common system.*

Here we must pay as many ogdens as there are new units of order zero required. The rest is found at no additional cost.

3 Estimation of the ogdens required to learn the Roman system of numeration.

Ogdens have to be paid for I, II, III, V, X, L, C, D, M; one for placing I before V and X to form IV and IX. One for placing I or II or III after each of the remaining signs, and two for indicating that the ogdens paid for I on the left can be used to indicate subtraction of the smaller one if it is placed on the left and addition when it is placed on the right. One ogden has to be paid for the convention of reading Roman numerals from the left, effecting as many steps backwards as there are signs followed by one or more which refer to a larger number, and another for adding if the one that follows refers to a smaller number.

Thus MCDXCIV or MDCCLXXIX require that these extra ogdens be paid.

---

* The array referred to is the table (T„) on page 16.

The capital investment for the Roman numerals in any language besides Latin is therefore eighteen (XVIII) ogdens. The returns are only MDCCCLXXXIX or one thousand eight hundred and eighty nine numerals.

4 Estimation of the cost of learning addition in any system of numeration.

- *In the common system.*

Ogdens need be paid only for the special attention to the correspondence between the set called 10 and a pair of complementary subsets. This represents indeed only two ogdens, one to recognize that, for example, 3 and 7 are complementary and one to recognize that from such a pair the pairs 2 and 8, and 4 and 6, can be derived (by say folding or unfolding fingers if the set of fingers is utilized as a model for 10, and folding as the process of generating complementary subsets.)

Another ogden is required to note that the relationship 4 + 6 ~ 10 leads to 40 + 60 ~ 100, 400 + 600 ~ 1000, etc., merely by placing 0's on the right of each of the written numerals. One more ogden is used to shift units from 40 or 60 to the other one producing, say, 41 + 59 ~ 42 + 58 ~ . . . 45 + 55 ~ 100, or between 400 and 600, 390 + 610 ~ 380 +620 ~ . . . ~ 1000.

One more ogden is required to note that when units of any order are shifted from one number to another in a pair of complements, the units of the same order add up to 9, except those on the extreme right, which add up to 10.

The cost of all additions is now quickly established through a number of transformations leading to the reading of the sum. Let us consider any example; the number of digits is not significant, only the implications of the transformations.

4865 +378	Since 135 is the complement of 865 in 1000 we shift these units from 378 to the first number and obtain a new
5000 +243	equivalent addition whose answer is immediately read as 5243

We need therefore to know:

- how to estimate complements of any numeral in the numeral containing as many 0's as the given numeral,
- how to shift that amount from one addend to the other,
- how to read the last addition.

Clearly in such a shifting of units we meet a subtraction — which is as it should be, since subtraction and addition are inverse operations which can be considered together from the start when we read complements. Hence one ogden has to be paid for learning to read additions as subtractions and subtractions as additions — at least in the case of complements within numerals containing as many zeros as they have digits minus one.

- *In another base.*

There is only one difference, not requiring any ogden, and that is to note that 9 must be replaced by the numerals preceding 10 in that base.

Hence after mastering numeration we can master additions for four ogdens provided we simultaneously master subtraction.

5 Estimation of the cost of learning subtraction in any base. Here instead of shifting an amount from one addend to the other we need to note:

- that complements like the ones we had before (in the common system) and which can be written for one ogden in the vertical form:

$$\begin{array}{r} 472 \\ +528 \\ \hline 1000 \end{array}$$ can be read for another ogden as

$$\begin{array}{r} 1000 \\ -528 \\ \hline 472 \end{array} \quad \text{or} \quad \begin{array}{r} 1000 \\ -472 \\ \hline 528 \end{array}$$

- that any subtraction can be transformed at no cost in ogdens as follows:

$$\begin{array}{r} 2016 \\ -478 \\ \hline \end{array} \quad 1016 + \begin{array}{r} 1000 \\ -478 \\ \hline \end{array} \quad 1016 + 522 \sim 1538$$

> by shifting 502 from the second to the first and adding 20.

In this paper we have not attempted to develop a teaching sequence, though as a consequence of our estimation of the cost of learning in ogdens we have found a procedure which actually suggests a route for teaching for mastery, understanding and swiftness. Details of the pedagogy will be given somewhere else. Here let us close by saying that by deliberately remaining within the fundamentals of mathematics we have been able to reach statements of extreme precision even if someone else's estimates do not agree exactly with the ones given here. That this is possible is the essence of the message written here.

Appendix B: A Map of Elementary Mathematics Derived From Tables of Partitions*

The contents of the table considered here can easily be seen to fall into four headings:

1 columns R_1 R_2 R_3 R_4;

2 the words in each column;

3 the arrows linking words;

4 the fusion of two columns at the bottom of the table.

---

* Reprinted from C. Gattegno, *For the teaching of mathematics*, vol. 3 (Reading, England: Educational Explorers, 1963.)

- The initial *R* stands for *restriction.* Though there are more than 4 principles of restriction, only these were considered necessary to provide the essence of the various constructions that would produce chapters of mathematics and hence sections of any elementary mathematics curriculum.

Appendix B:
A Map of Elementary Mathematics Derived From Tables of Partitions

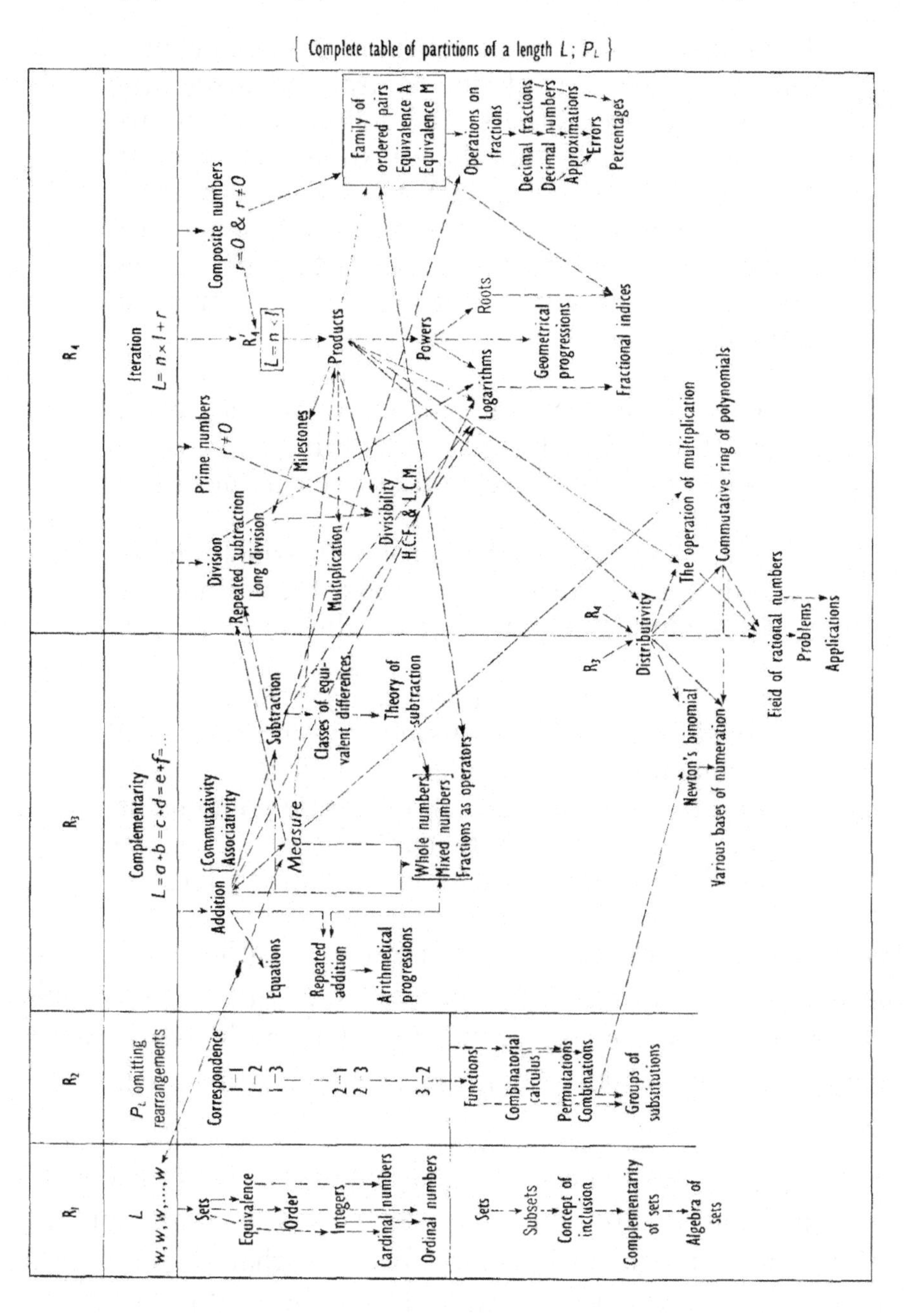

R_1 appears first from an arbitrary personal choice and not because of its logical or structural precedence over others. Its definition is in the equivalence of L and the maximal set of rods forming a train equivalent to L — i.e. a train composed of white rods. It is also the first and last line of the table of partitions P_L starting with L and ending with the same length made of the greatest number of rods.

- R_2 is another restriction on the set of partitions. It is formed by ignoring all possible *permutations* of a set of rods in each line of P_L.

- R_3 is the restriction on P_L which allows only lines formed of two rods; these lines are thus complementary to each other in L.

- R_4 is the last restriction on P_L we must consider before we can study the *main* ideas of elementary mathematics. It is formed of all *iterated* lengths; that is, each line contains as many rods of a particular length $< L$ as are needed to form L exactly, or most nearly form it.

Having selected these four ways of producing basic ideas, I chose the words in each column to represent the various permissible interpretations, or the various chapters that can be begun, when only the concept embedded in the restriction is being used.

R_1 clearly provides the classical foundation for arithmetic since the repetition of the unit has served as a basis for the elaboration of integers, which then form sets that are recognized to serve for cardinal and ordinal purposes. But in R_1 we recognize that, if instead of considering numbers we consider the sets formed by the white rods equivalent to the successive *L*'s, other possibilities also exist.

R_1 indicates how the rods could serve to generate the traditional approach to mathematics in schools. Thus, by ignoring all the other rods and what they can bring, we can provide a curriculum equivalent to the classical treatment of number. This shows us that we cannot lose much of what traditionalists want, since this is equivalent to a very special use of P_L; moreover, we may expect a great deal more if we can introduce other ideas and other materials with new uses.

R_2 indicates how the simple fact of noticing that the same rods may appear in various lines of P_L can generate new insights into how sets can be related. If we agree to use any one line to represent the set of all the permutations of the rods in that line, we shall have generated many examples of correspondences 1 to 1,1 to 2 or 2 to 1, and so on. The modern notion of function in analysis can thus be brought to the notice of beginners as a special awareness of a very immediate kind: the multiple correspondences between elements of sets. But because they are at hand, the permutations thus singled out can be studied, and likewise their transformations, which lead to a study of the group of substitutions. Combinatorial algebra in its other aspects is also open and requires no new techniques of computation.

R_3 is third simply for reasons of order and display; it is more primitive than R_1 or R_2. Here, the study of complementarity is taken as far as it seems possible at the elementary level. It can be seen that the set of R_3's, if combined with itself, generates the set of *PL*'s, thus telling us both how fundamental complementarity is, and also that indeed nothing is lost in analysis at this level if we substitute the study of $\{R_3\}$ for that of $\{P_L\}$.

But because R_3 is based on addition, the content described is a development of aspects of this operation.

R_4 is, in short, a study of multiplication and what it generates that is not directly visible in addition. In this table there are three features that need to be brought into relief:

1. the place of measure;
2. a restriction within a restriction, or R_4';
3. the mutual impact of R_3 and R_4.

Measure, in the work with the rods, is borrowed from physics and introduces counting by the back door, since it is necessary to know *how many* times the unit has been used to associate a number with a given length. But measure is also the source of fractions and mixed numbers, and serves later to introduce real numbers. Thus measure is a more powerful tool than counting, which it uses as a generator of mathematics. Counting is met in R_1 and can be interpreted again as being a measure with white rods. Measure is naturally also an interpretation of iteration and is the basis of R_4 and all its consequences.

If $\{R_4\}$ is produced out of $\{PL\}$ by a consideration of iterations, R'_4 still further restricts the set by retaining in it the measures that are "successful" or do not require a remainder. This way of creating chapters by restriction on restriction is obviously present at many points of the table, though not singled out expressly by a name.

Finally, the bottom part of the table indicates another procedure, that of relating the two processes of R_3 and R_4 through a special link, here shown as the distributive law or a new axiom. It opens up a number of more structured chapters which go to form the complex body of elementary mathematics and which is therefore the aim of study in elementary schools.

To conclude this explanatory sketch of what has been put into the table, a word can be added about the arrows. They serve two purposes: they not only indicate routes from one place to another, but also link these places together, making them logically dependent. It would be an interesting exercise (and one which I shall leave to the reader) to find out how many *different* routes can be produced using the arrows provided in the table. Some of them could serve as alternative curricula to use with different classes for the conquest of mathematics. What matters here is that the reader can see how to structure a curriculum. What must be watched is the order needed for the presentation of the notions and techniques; this is provided by the arrows and the stations (or chapters) in the course of study.

Let us note that other uses of the rods exist which are not mentioned in the table, but which can be the object of additional restrictions. Thus, the study of simultaneous equations can, for instance, form an R_5.

Books and Materials

Other books by the same author of particular interest to teachers of mathematics include:

What We Owe Children (New York: Outerbridge and Dienstfrey, 1970.) An outline of a scientific approach to teaching.

For the Teaching of Mathematics, vols. 1-3 (Reading, England: Educational Explorers, 1963-64.) Collected articles on a variety of topics in mathematics education.

Gattegno Mathematics, Books 1-7 (New York: Educational Solutions, 1969-73.) A complete program of elementary mathematics based on the use of *Algebricks* and geoboards.

These books, as well as sets of *Algebricks,* geoboards, and mathematical films (*Animated Geometry* and *Folklore of Mathematics,*) are obtainable from Educational Solutions Inc., www.EducationalSolutions.com.

Lightning Source UK Ltd.
Milton Keynes UK
UKOW07f1839071117
312368UK00005B/109/P

9 780878 252206